SCOTT FORESMAN · ADDISON WESLEY

Mathematics

GRADE 2

TENNESSEE

TENNESSEE

D1489823

Tennessee Daily Practice and TCAP Test Prep

Table of Contents

Cover: Bob Kerr

ISBN: 0-328-10390-X

1 2 3 4 5 6 7 8 9 10 V084 13 12 11 10 09 08 07 06 05 04

Lesson 1-1   Name _____

1 How many Tennessee honeybees in all?

4 and 3 is _____ in all.

43	7	6	1
Ⓐ	Ⓑ	Ⓒ	Ⓓ

---

2 Which sentence tells how many stars in all?

Ⓐ 7 and 1 is 8 in all.

Ⓑ 7 and 3 is 10 in all.

Ⓒ 7 and 7 is 14 in all.

Ⓓ 9 and 2 is 11 in all.

3

9   and   _____   is   11   in all.

2	5	9	11
Ⓐ	Ⓑ	Ⓒ	Ⓓ

---

4 Howard has 2 basketballs and 4 footballs.
How many balls in all?

4	5	6	7
Ⓐ	Ⓑ	Ⓒ	Ⓓ

---

5 4 and 8 is _____ in all.

4	9	12	14
Ⓐ	Ⓑ	Ⓒ	Ⓓ

1

Lesson 1-2   Name _____

1 Solve: $3 + 4$	**2** Solve: $4 + 6$
5 6 7 9	5 6 8 10
Ⓐ Ⓑ Ⓒ Ⓓ	Ⓐ Ⓑ Ⓒ Ⓓ

3 There are 5 black cars and 3 white cars.
How many cars in all?

$2 + 3 = 5$ $5 + 5 = 10$ $8 + 2 = 10$ $5 + 3 = 8$
   Ⓐ   Ⓑ   Ⓒ   Ⓓ

4 There are 3 large dogs and 8 small dogs in the park.
How many dogs in all?

11   9   5   2
Ⓐ   Ⓑ   Ⓒ   Ⓓ

5 Write a story that uses the addition sentence $4 + 8 = 12$.

Lesson 1-3   Name _____

1 Ray has 2 postage stamps.
Enrico has 5 postage stamps.
Which number sentence shows
how many postage stamps in all?

$5 + 7 = 12$ $5 + 5 = 10$ $2 + 5 = 7$ $7 + 2 = 9$
Ⓐ   Ⓑ   Ⓒ   Ⓓ

---

2 Beth has 4 postcards from Nashville and 6 from Chattanooga.
Which sentence shows how many postcards she has in all?

$6 - 4 = 2$ $6 + 6 = 12$ $5 + 5 = 10$ $4 + 6 = 10$
Ⓐ   Ⓑ   Ⓒ   Ⓓ

---

3 Mica read 6 books last week and 6 books this week.
How many books did Mica read in all?

6   8   10   12
Ⓐ   Ⓑ   Ⓒ   Ⓓ

---

4 Mrs. Lewis baked 9 corn muffins and 3 bran muffins.
How many muffins did she bake in all?

$9 + 3 =$ _____

9   12   13   14
Ⓐ   Ⓑ   Ⓒ   Ⓓ

---

5 Sam has 4 pencils in his book bag. He has 4 pencils in his desk.
How many pencils does he have in all?

$4 + 4 =$ _____

0   4   8   9
Ⓐ   Ⓑ   Ⓒ   Ⓓ

Lesson 1-4   Name _____

1   3 take away 1 is _____.

    2   3   4   6
   Ⓐ   Ⓑ   Ⓒ   Ⓓ

2   9 take away 4 is _____.

    11   8   5   4
   Ⓐ   Ⓑ   Ⓒ   Ⓓ

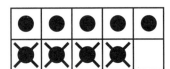

3   Which sentence tells how many are left?

   Ⓐ   4 and 6 is 10 in all.

   Ⓑ   10 take away 6 is 4.

   Ⓒ   10 and 4 is 14 in all.

   Ⓓ   6 take away 4 is 2.

4   12 take away 9 is _____.

    3   4   6   9
   Ⓐ   Ⓑ   Ⓒ   Ⓓ

5   Write a subtraction sentence that matches the picture.

   _____ ◯ _____ ◯ _____

4

Lesson 1-5   Name _____

1 How many blocks should be taken away to have 5 left?

2   3   4   5
Ⓐ   Ⓑ   Ⓒ   Ⓓ

---

2 How many more black beads than white beads are there?

1   2   3   4
Ⓐ   Ⓑ   Ⓒ   Ⓓ

---

3 How many more letters in Nashville than in Memphis?

MEMPHIS   NASHVILLE

4   3   2   1
Ⓐ   Ⓑ   Ⓒ   Ⓓ

---

4 Mary has visited Graceland 5 times. Julie has visited 3 times. How many more times has Mary visited Graceland?

6   5   3   2
Ⓐ   Ⓑ   Ⓒ   Ⓓ

---

5 Write a subtraction story for this fact.

$7 - 3 = \boxed{}$

Lesson 1-6   Name _____

1 Reilly has 4 sticker books. He gave 2 sticker books to his sister. How many sticker books does he have left?

$4 - 2 = \square$

1	2	3	4
Ⓐ	Ⓑ	Ⓒ	Ⓓ

2 Kelly has 3 apples. She eats one of them. How many apples are left?

$3 - 1 = \square$

1	2	3	4
Ⓐ	Ⓑ	Ⓒ	Ⓓ

3 A store in Memphis sold 9 newspapers on Monday and 8 newspapers on Tuesday. How many more were sold on Monday?

17	9	8	1
Ⓐ	Ⓑ	Ⓒ	Ⓓ

4 There are 11 potatoes in a bag. Mrs. Franks uses 4 for dinner. How many are left?

4	5	6	7
Ⓐ	B	Ⓒ	Ⓓ

5 Madison has 6 pencils. She gave 2 to Jim. Which sentence shows how many Madison has left?

$4 + 2 = 6$	$6 \div 2 = 3$	$6 - 2 = 4$	$6 + 2 = 8$
Ⓐ	Ⓑ	Ⓒ	Ⓓ

Lesson 1-7   Name _____

1 Which sentence is the same as 7 take away 4 is 3?

$7 - 4 = 3$ $7 + 3 = 10$ $7 - 3 = 4$ $3 + 4 = 7$
Ⓐ   Ⓑ   Ⓒ   Ⓓ

---

2 5 ducks were in the pond.
Now there are 4.
How many flew away?

| 1 | 4 | 5 | 9 |
| Ⓐ | Ⓑ | Ⓒ | Ⓓ |

---

3 There are 6 toy cars and 2 toy trucks. How many toys in all?

____ ◯ ____ ◯ ____

4   6   8   9
Ⓐ   Ⓑ   Ⓒ   Ⓓ

---

4 There are 6 girls and 4 boys on the baseball team. Which
expression shows how many people are on the team in all?

$6 + 4$ $7 - 3$ $4 + 1$ $9 - 4$
Ⓐ   Ⓑ   Ⓒ   Ⓓ

---

5 There were 10 cows in the barn. Then 4 cows walked out of the barn.
How many cows are left in the barn? Write a number sentence.

____ ◯ ____ ◯ ____

7

Accomplishments 2.1.2.d. Write and explain related addition and subtraction sentences.
*2.1.3.d. Add … efficiently and accurately with single-digit numbers.
2.2.4.a. Apply the commutative property of addition.

Lesson I-8   Name _____

I What is the related addition fact? $2 + 3 = 5$ △ △ △ △ △

$5 + 2 = 7$ ⒶＡ $5 - 3 = 2$ Ⓑ $3 + 2 = 5$ Ⓒ $3 + 3 = 6$ Ⓓ

---

2 What is the missing number?

_____ $+ 5 = 11$ $5 +$ _____ $= 11$

5 Ⓐ   6 Ⓑ   7 Ⓒ   8 Ⓓ

---

3 What is the missing number?

_____ $+ 4 = 6$ $6 - 4 =$ _____

10 Ⓐ   6 Ⓑ   4 Ⓒ   2 Ⓓ

---

4 Which number sentence does <u>not</u> have a related addition fact?

$4 + 5 = 9$ Ⓐ $4 + 4 = 8$ Ⓑ $4 + 3 = 7$ Ⓒ $4 + 8 = 12$ Ⓓ

---

5 Which two sentences match the picture?   ★ ★ ★ ☆

$4 + 1 = 5$
$1 + 4 = 5$
Ⓐ

$3 + 1 = 4$
$1 + 3 = 4$
Ⓑ

$4 + 3 = 7$
$3 + 4 = 7$
Ⓒ

$4 + 4 = 8$
$3 + 1 = 4$
Ⓓ

© Pearson Education, Inc. 2

8

Accomplishments 2.1.2.d. Write and explain related addition and subtraction sentences.
*2.1.3.d. Add … efficiently and accurately with single-digit numbers.

Lesson 1-9   Name _____

---

1   What is the sum of 9 and 1 ?

| 6 | 8 | 9 | 10 |
| Ⓐ | Ⓑ | Ⓒ | Ⓓ |

---

2   Which does <u>not</u> have a sum of 10?

| 2 + 8 | 5 + 5 | 6 + 3 | 1 + 9 |
| Ⓐ | Ⓑ | Ⓒ | Ⓓ |

---

3   What number is missing from both facts?

$$3 + \underline{\hspace{1cm}} = 10 \qquad 10 - 3 = \underline{\hspace{1cm}}$$

| 10 | 8 | 7 | 5 |
| Ⓐ | Ⓑ | Ⓒ | Ⓓ |

---

4   Rose needs 10 points to win the game.
She has 3 points. How many more points
does Rose need to win the game?

| 4 | 6 | 7 | 8 |
| Ⓐ | Ⓑ | Ⓒ | Ⓓ |

---

5   There are 10 marbles in all. How many
are in the bag?

| 4 | 6 | 8 | 10 |
| Ⓐ | Ⓑ | Ⓒ | Ⓓ |

Accomplishments 2.1.2.d. Write and explain related addition and subtraction sentences.
*2.1.3.d. Add … efficiently and accurately with single-digit numbers.
2.2.3.a. Interpret and solve open sentences that involve addition….

Lesson 1-10   Name _____

---

1 Which sentence is in this fact family?

$2 + 3 = 5$
$5 - 3 = 2$
$3 + 2 = 5$

$4 + 1 = 5$ $5 - 1 = 4$ $5 - 2 = 3$ $5 + 3 = 8$
Ⓐ   Ⓑ   Ⓒ   Ⓓ

---

2 Which picture matches this fact family?

$4 + 2 = 6$ $6 - 4 = 2$
$2 + 4 = 6$ $6 - 2 = 4$

○○●●   ●●●●○○○○   ○●   ○○○○○●●
Ⓐ   Ⓑ   Ⓒ   Ⓓ

---

3 Which is the related subtraction fact? $5 + 7 = 12$

$7 + 5 = 12$ $12 - 5 = 7$ $12 - 4 = 8$ $8 + 4 = 12$
Ⓐ   Ⓑ   Ⓒ   Ⓓ

---

4 Which fact is <u>not</u> in the same fact family as $3 + 4 = 7$?

$7 - 4 = 3$ $7 - 3 = 4$ $7 - 2 = 5$ $4 + 3 = 7$
Ⓐ   Ⓑ   Ⓒ   Ⓓ

---

5 Write all the other number sentences in this fact family:

$1 + 5 = 6$

___ ◯ ___ ◯ ___   ___ ◯ ___ ◯ ___

___ ◯ ___ ◯ ___

Lesson 1-11   Name _____

1 There were 12 eggs in all. Brent used 3 for breakfast. How many are left in the carton?

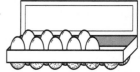

_____ + 3 = 12

3	5	8	9
Ⓐ	Ⓑ	Ⓒ	Ⓓ

2 What number is missing? _____ + 5 = 9

4	5	6	7
Ⓐ	Ⓑ	Ⓒ	Ⓓ

3 Ariella got 6 birthday gifts. She has opened 5 of her gifts. How many does she have left to open?

5 + _____ = 6

5	3	2	1
Ⓐ	Ⓑ	Ⓒ	Ⓓ

4 Mike has 8 shirts. In his closet are 2 clean shirts. How many shirts are in the laundry?

2 + _____ = 8

10	8	6	4
Ⓐ	Ⓑ	Ⓒ	Ⓓ

5 Which two addends make 7?

5 and 3	2 and 5	1 and 4	7 and 7
Ⓐ	Ⓑ	Ⓒ	Ⓓ

11

Accomplishments 2.1.2.c. Write and identify number sentences that describe situations involving addition and subtraction.
*2.1.3.a. Solve story problems involving numbers to 100.
*2.1.3.d. Add and subtract efficiently and accurately with single-digit numbers.

Lesson 1-12   Name _____

1 Solve: 5 + 4

9	8	7	4
(A)	(B)	(C)	(D)

---

2 Rita drew 3 circles. She then erased 1 circle. How many circles were left?

Which sentence helps solve this problem?

1 + 3 = 4	4 − 3 = 1	3 − 1 = 2	3 + 2 = 5
(A)	(B)	(C)	(D)

---

3 Rita drew 3 circles. She then erased 1 circle. How many circles are left?

Which picture matches this problem?

OO	OOOO	OO⊠	⊠⊠⊠O
(A)	(B)	(C)	(D)

---

4 Spot and Milo are dogs. A dog has 4 legs. How many legs in all?

_____ ◯ _____ ◯ _____

4 + 0 = 4	4 + 4 = 8	5 + 5 = 10	2 + 2 = 4
(A)	(B)	(C)	(D)

---

5 Write your own story that matches 2 + 1 = 3.

Draw a picture.

Lesson 2-1   Name _____

1   Count on to find the sum.

9 + 2 =

   2   7   11   12
  Ⓐ   Ⓑ   Ⓒ   Ⓓ

2   What is the next number in the pattern?

7, 9, 11, _____

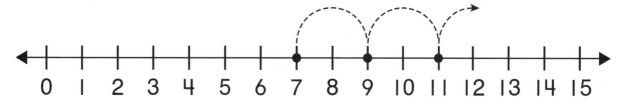

   7   12   13   17
  Ⓐ   Ⓑ   Ⓒ   Ⓓ

3   Vera bought 8 postcards from Nashville. Jared bought 3 postcards. How many postcards do they have together?

   9   10   11   12
  Ⓐ   Ⓑ   Ⓒ   Ⓓ

4   There are 5 dogs sleeping. There are 2 dogs running. How many dogs in all?

   4   5   6   7
  Ⓐ   Ⓑ   Ⓒ   Ⓓ

5   **Solve:**   9 + 5 = _____

   14   12   9   4
  Ⓐ   Ⓑ   Ⓒ   Ⓓ

Lesson 2-2   Name _____

1 Which double has a sum of 14?

△ △ △ △ △ △ △
△ △ △ △ △ △ △

9 + 5   7 + 7   5 + 5   7 + 2
Ⓐ   Ⓑ   Ⓒ   Ⓓ

---

2 Which sentence is <u>not</u> a doubles fact?

2 + 2 = 4   5 + 5 = 10   8 + 2 = 10   6 + 6 = 12
Ⓐ   Ⓑ   Ⓒ   Ⓓ

---

3 Ashley has 3 dogs and 3 cats.
How many pets does Ashley have in all?

4   5   6   33
Ⓐ   Ⓑ   Ⓒ   Ⓓ

---

4 Todd walks 5 blocks to school and 5 blocks home each
day. How many blocks does Todd walk each day?

0   10   15   20
Ⓐ   Ⓑ   Ⓒ   Ⓓ

---

5 Draw a doubles fact with 8 birds. Put the same number
of birds in each nest. Then write the doubles fact.

_____ + _____ = _____

14

Lesson 2-3   Name _____

1 Which doubles fact can you use to help find 7 + 8?

$$7 + 7 = 14 \qquad 5 + 5 = 10 \qquad 2 + 2 = 4 \qquad 9 + 9 = 18$$
    Ⓐ   Ⓑ   Ⓒ   Ⓓ

2 **Solve:**   6 + 6 = _____

66	16	12	6
Ⓐ	Ⓑ	Ⓒ	Ⓓ

3 **Solve:**   6 + 7 = _____

13	12	10	7
Ⓐ	Ⓑ	Ⓒ	Ⓓ

4 What doubles fact can help you find 4 + 3?

$$7 + 7 = 14 \qquad 5 + 5 = 10 \qquad 1 + 1 = 2 \qquad 3 + 3 = 6$$
    Ⓐ   Ⓑ   Ⓒ   Ⓓ

5 What doubles fact can help you find 6 + 5?

$$6 + 6 = 12 \qquad 5 + 5 = 10 \qquad 4 + 4 = 8 \qquad 12 = 6 + 6$$
    Ⓐ   Ⓑ   Ⓒ   Ⓓ

6 What doubles fact can help you find 5 + 4?

$$5 + 5 = 10 \qquad 4 + 4 = 8 \qquad 5 + 3 = 8 \qquad 3 + 3 = 6$$
    Ⓐ   Ⓑ   Ⓒ   Ⓓ

Lesson 2-4   Name _____

1 **Solve:**   2 + 5 + 5 = _____

7   10   12   14
Ⓐ   Ⓑ   Ⓒ   Ⓓ

---

2 **Solve:**   6 + 1 + 6 = _____

6   7   12   13
Ⓐ   Ⓑ   Ⓒ   Ⓓ

---

3 **Solve:**   9 + 3 + 1 = _____

4   10   13   14
Ⓐ   Ⓑ   Ⓒ   Ⓓ

---

4 What number is missing?

3 + 5 + _____ = 10

1   2   4   5
Ⓐ   Ⓑ   Ⓒ   Ⓓ

---

5 How many pieces of fruit are needed to make fruit salad?

_____ _____ _____ _____

5   9   10   14
Ⓐ   Ⓑ   Ⓒ   Ⓓ

| Fruit Salad |
| Recipe |
| 2 apples |
| 3 bananas |
| 4 plums |

Lesson 2-5   Name _____

1 Solve: 9 + 4 = _____

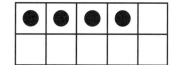

Ⓐ 12

Ⓑ 13

Ⓒ 14

Ⓓ 15

2 Solve: 9 + 6 = _____

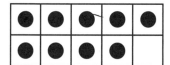 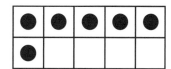

Ⓐ 15

Ⓑ 14

Ⓒ 13

Ⓓ 3

3 There are 8 cows in the barn. 9 cows are in the field.
       How many cows in all?

1	16	17	18
Ⓐ	Ⓑ	Ⓒ	Ⓓ

4 What number makes this sentence true?

_____ + 9 = 14

6	5	3	2
Ⓐ	Ⓑ	Ⓒ	Ⓓ

5 Explain how making 10 helps you find 9 + 2.

_____

_____

_____

Lesson 2-6   Name _____

1 **Solve:**   8 + 5 = _____

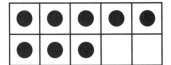

Ⓐ   8

Ⓑ   12

Ⓒ   13

Ⓓ   14

2 **Solve:**   8 + 3 = _____

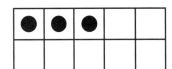

Ⓐ   11

Ⓑ   12

Ⓒ   13

Ⓓ   83

3 What is the missing number?

8 + 6 = 10 + _____

14	9	8	4
Ⓐ	Ⓑ	Ⓒ	Ⓓ

4 What is the missing number?

9 + _____ = 13

4	5	6	13
Ⓐ	Ⓑ	Ⓒ	Ⓓ

5 Kari has 6 dolls. Sara has 7 dolls. How many dolls do the girls have in all?

7	12	13	15
Ⓐ	Ⓑ	Ⓒ	Ⓓ

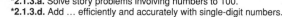
Accomplishments 2.1.2.c. Write and identify number sentences that describe situations involving addition....
***2.1.3.a.** Solve story problems involving numbers to 100.
***2.1.3.d.** Add ... efficiently and accurately with single-digit numbers.

Lesson 2-7   Name _____

The children at Johnson School voted on their favorite food. Use the table for questions 1 and 2.

Favorite Foods

	Pizza	BBQ Chicken	Hot Dogs
Grade 1	6	7	6
Grade 2	5	2	9
Grade 3	4	7	5

1 How many children like BBQ Chicken best?

7 + _____ + _____ = _____

7	9	14	16
Ⓐ	Ⓑ	Ⓒ	Ⓓ

---

2 How many children are there in grade 3?

20	16	15	4
Ⓐ	Ⓑ	Ⓒ	Ⓓ

---

3 Which expression has a sum of 11?

5 + 6	5 + 7	8 + 4	1 + 1
Ⓐ	Ⓑ	Ⓒ	Ⓓ

---

4 Which expression can help you find 9 + 4?

6 + 4	10 + 3	4 + 4	8 + 2
Ⓐ	Ⓑ	Ⓒ	Ⓓ

---

5 Write a number sentence for this story. Tom ate 6 strawberries. Alexis ate 7 strawberries. How many strawberries did they eat in all?

_____ + _____ = _____

Lesson 2-8   Name _____

1 What is the next number in the pattern? 5, 4, 3, _____

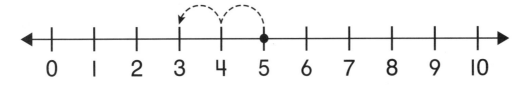

4   2   1   0
Ⓐ   Ⓑ   Ⓒ   Ⓓ

2 Solve: $9 - 2 =$ _____

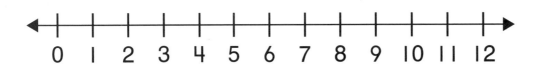

11   10   8   7
Ⓐ   Ⓑ   Ⓒ   Ⓓ

3 Jim has 6 stickers. He gives 2 stickers to his sister. How many stickers does Jim have left?

3   4   5   6
Ⓐ   Ⓑ   Ⓒ   Ⓓ

4 Mrs. Quinn made 9 dinner rolls. Mr. Quinn ate 2 rolls with his dinner. How many dinner rolls are left?

2   7   10   12
Ⓐ   Ⓑ   Ⓒ   Ⓓ

5 There are 9 children at the park. Then 3 children go home. How many children are still at the park?

6   5   4   3
Ⓐ   Ⓑ   Ⓒ   Ⓓ

Lesson 2-9   Name _____

1 What doubles fact can help you find 12 − 6?

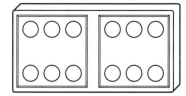

$6 + 3 = 9$ $8 + 8 = 16$ $6 + 6 = 12$ $5 + 5 = 10$
Ⓐ   Ⓑ   Ⓒ   Ⓓ

---

2 What doubles fact can help you find 10 − 5?

$10 + 10 = 20$ $8 + 8 = 16$ $9 + 9 = 18$ $5 + 5 = 10$
Ⓐ   Ⓑ   Ⓒ   Ⓓ

---

3 Steven has 6 cookies. He wants to give 3 of them to Brittney. Which sentence matches this story?

$3 + 6 = 9$ $6 + 3 = 9$ $6 − 2 = 4$ $6 − 3 = 3$
Ⓐ   Ⓑ   Ⓒ   Ⓓ

---

4 **Solve:** $18 − 9 = $ _____

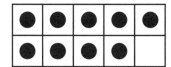 

Ⓐ   0

Ⓑ   8

Ⓒ   9

Ⓓ   10

---

5 There are 14 pieces of gum in all. How can Leo and Julie share the gum so they each have an <u>equal</u> number of pieces? Write a sentence to solve this problem.

Accomplishments 2.1.2.d. Write and explain related addition and subtraction sentences.
*2.1.3.d. Add and subtract efficiently and accurately with single-digit numbers.
2.2.3.a. Interpret and solve open sentences that involve addition or subtraction.

Lesson 2-10   Name _____

1 What addition fact is related to 5 − 1 = 4?

$4 + 1 = 5$ $5 + 1 = 4$ $5 − 4 = 1$ $5 + 4 = 9$
Ⓐ   Ⓑ   Ⓒ   Ⓓ

---

2 What is the missing number?

$12 − \underline{\hphantom{000}} = 3$ $3 + \underline{\hphantom{000}} = 12$

10   9   8   7
Ⓐ   Ⓑ   Ⓒ   Ⓓ

---

3 What addition fact can be used to find 12 − 4?

$10 + 2 = 12$ $7 + 5 = 12$ $8 + 4 = 12$ $11 + 1 = 12$
Ⓐ   Ⓑ   Ⓒ   Ⓓ

---

4 Bob milks 13 cows each morning. He has already milked 4 cows this morning. How many more cows does Bob need to milk?

$13 − 4 = \underline{\hphantom{000}}$ $4 + \underline{\hphantom{000}} = 13$

17   9   7   3
Ⓐ   Ⓑ   Ⓒ   Ⓓ

---

5 There are 3 cars in all. How many cars are in the garage?

1   2   4   5
Ⓐ   Ⓑ   Ⓒ   Ⓓ

Lesson 2-11   Name _____

1 What does the ⬜ weigh?

$6 + 5 =$ _____

- Ⓐ 5 pounds
- Ⓑ 6 pounds
- Ⓒ 11 pounds
- Ⓓ 13 pounds

---

2 What does the ⬭ weigh?

$10 - 2 =$ _____ $2 +$ _____ $= 10$

2 pounds	5 pounds	8 pounds	9 pounds
Ⓐ	Ⓑ	Ⓒ	Ⓓ

---

3 What does the △ weigh?

_____ $+ 8 = 15$

4 pounds	5 pounds	6 pounds	7 pounds
Ⓐ	Ⓑ	Ⓒ	Ⓓ

---

4 What is the missing number?

_____ $+ 9 = 16$ $16 - 9 =$ _____

7	6	5	4
Ⓐ	Ⓑ	Ⓒ	Ⓓ

---

5 What is the missing number?

$2 +$ _____ $+ 3 = 10$

5	4	3	2
Ⓐ	Ⓑ	Ⓒ	Ⓓ

Accomplishments **2.1.2.c.** Write…number sentences that describe situations…. ***2.1.3.a.** Solve story problems….
*2.1.3.d. Add and subtract … with single-digit numbers. ***2.1.3.e.** Use a variety of strategies and representation to add….
2.2.3.a. Interpret and solve open sentences….

Lesson 2-12   Name _____

1 Mr. Butler's 2nd grade class made this table. How many children visited these three places?

Places Visited During Summer

Grand Ole Opry	2
Alex Haley's Boyhood Home	9
Great Smoky Mountains National Park	5

(A) 5

(B) 9

(C) 11

(D) 16

---

2 Molly found 5 pinecones and 4 acorns. Which number sentence describes this?

$1 + 3 = 4$ $4 + 4 = 8$ $5 + 4 = 9$ $3 + 3 = 6$

(A)   (B)   (C)   (D)

---

3 What is the missing number? _____ $+ 7 = 12$

5   6   7   8

(A)   (B)   (C)   (D)

---

4 **Solve:** $14 - 9 =$ _____

4   5   6   7

(A)   (B)   (C)   (D)

---

5 Write two related subtraction facts for $2 + 3 = 5$.

____ ◯ ____ ◯ ____

____ ◯ ____ ◯ ____

Lesson 3-1   Name _____

1 How many in all?

_____ tens and _____ ones is _____ in all.

32	23	10	3
Ⓐ	Ⓑ	Ⓒ	Ⓓ

---

2 What number is missing?

21	22	23	24	25	26	27	28	29	30
31	32	33	34	35	36	37	38	39	

39	40	41	50
Ⓐ	Ⓑ	Ⓒ	Ⓓ

---

3 How many peas in all?

10	14	16	20
Ⓐ	Ⓑ	Ⓒ	Ⓓ

---

4 Which number is greater than 45?

9	40	45	54
Ⓐ	Ⓑ	Ⓒ	Ⓓ

---

5 Circle the groups of ten.
Count the tens and ones.
Write the numbers.

_____ tens and _____ ones is _____ in all.

25

Accomplishments 2.1.1.c. Read and write numerals to 999. ***2.1.1.d.** Recognize the place value of the a digit in numbers to 999. ***2.1.1.l.** Represent numbers to 999 using flexible ways using a variety of materials. (e.g., 23 as 23 ones, 1 ten and 13 ones, and/or 2 tens and 3 ones).

Lesson 3-2   Name _____

1   How many in all?

   Ⓐ   8

   Ⓑ   11

   Ⓒ   83

   Ⓓ   803

---

2   What number has 5 tens and 9 ones?

   59   50   14   9
   Ⓐ   Ⓑ   Ⓒ   Ⓓ

---

3   Six children have how many fingers in all?

   6   10   12   60
   Ⓐ   Ⓑ   Ⓒ   Ⓓ

---

4   What number am I? My tens digit is one more than 3.
My ones digit is 2 + 5.

   73   47   37   32
   Ⓐ   Ⓑ   Ⓒ   Ⓓ

---

5   What do 4 tens and 9 ones equal?

   Ⓐ   94

   Ⓑ   50

   Ⓒ   49

   Ⓓ   45

Lesson 3-3   Name _____

1 Two + twelve =

_____ ◯ _____ ◯ _____

14	10	6	2
Ⓐ	Ⓑ	Ⓒ	Ⓓ

2 The number word for 35 is _____.

Ⓐ three-five

Ⓑ thirty-five

Ⓒ three-fifty

Ⓓ fifty-three

3 Sixty-two is the number word for _____.

62	66	602	622
Ⓐ	Ⓑ	Ⓒ	Ⓓ

4 Name the tens digit in twenty-five.

25	20	5	2
Ⓐ	Ⓑ	Ⓒ	Ⓓ

5 What number word is ten more than forty?

Ⓐ forty-one

Ⓑ forty-five

Ⓒ fifty

Ⓓ fifty-four

Accomplishments *2.1.1.l. Represent numbers to 999 using flexible ways using a variety of materials (e.g., 23 as 23 ones, 1 ten and 13 ones, and/or 2 tens and 3 ones). **2.1.3.f.** Explain and justify solution strategies used in problem solving.

Lesson 3-4   Name _____

1 Which number completes the table?

   Ⓐ 2

   Ⓑ 3

   Ⓒ 6

   Ⓓ 7

Tens	Tens	Total
0	6	60
1	5	60
2	4	60
3		60

---

2 Find the pattern. What are the missing numbers?

30, 40, 50, _____, _____, _____

  60, 70, 80   50, 40, 30   51, 52, 53   60, 70, 90

     Ⓐ   Ⓑ   Ⓒ   Ⓓ

---

3 Which number is the <u>greatest</u>?

  59   89   69   99

  Ⓐ   Ⓑ   Ⓒ   Ⓓ

---

4 Which makes 70?

  7 + 0   7 + 10   40 + 20   50 + 20

   Ⓐ   Ⓑ   Ⓒ   Ⓓ

---

5 How many in all?

 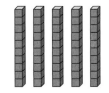

  Ⓐ   3 + 5 = 8

  Ⓑ   30 + 50 = 80

  Ⓒ   10 + 50 = 60

  Ⓓ   35

Lesson 3-5　　Name _____

1 Which matches twenty-seven is less than forty-two?

Ⓐ　$27 + 42$

Ⓑ　$27 = 42$

Ⓒ　$27 > 42$

Ⓓ　$27 < 42$

2 Which statement is true?

Ⓐ　$63 < 36$

Ⓑ　$51 > 50$

Ⓒ　$36 > 63$

Ⓓ　$51 < 50$

3 Which symbol makes this statement true?

$13 \bigcirc 31$

$<$	$=$	$>$	@
Ⓐ	Ⓑ	Ⓒ	Ⓓ

4 What number makes a true statement?

_____ > 48

36	40	48	84
Ⓐ	Ⓑ	Ⓒ	Ⓓ

5 Write 3 true statements.

_____ $<$ _____　　　_____ $=$ _____　　　_____ $>$ _____

Lesson 3-6   Name _____

1 What number is closest to 60?

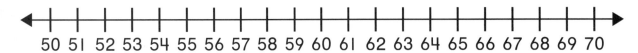

68   62   55   52
Ⓐ   Ⓑ   Ⓒ   Ⓓ

---

2 72 is closest to _____?

70   75   80   90
Ⓐ   Ⓑ   Ⓒ   Ⓓ

---

3 47 is between _____ and _____.

40 and 45   40 and 50   50 and 60   60 and 70
    Ⓐ   Ⓑ   Ⓒ   Ⓓ

---

4 Almost 50 tickets were sold for the school's talent show.
Which number could be the exact number of tickets sold?

40   45   49   53
Ⓐ   Ⓑ   Ⓒ   Ⓓ

---

5 Mai lives 21 miles from Knoxville. Which number shows
about how far Mai lives from Knoxville?

10   20   30   40
Ⓐ   Ⓑ   Ⓒ   Ⓓ

30

Lesson 3-7   Name _____

1 What is the missing number?

33, 34, _____, 36

33	34	35	37
Ⓐ	Ⓑ	Ⓒ	Ⓓ

---

2 One before 60 is _____.

58	59	61	62
Ⓐ	Ⓑ	Ⓒ	Ⓓ

---

3 What number is between 21 and 23?

20	22	24	25
Ⓐ	Ⓑ	Ⓒ	Ⓓ

---

4 What is the missing number?

46	54	55	66
Ⓐ	Ⓑ	Ⓒ	Ⓓ

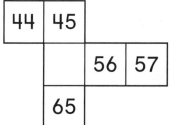

---

5 Ashley wrote a book. She is writing the page number at the bottom of each page. What number should Ashley write after page 19?

18	20	29	30
Ⓐ	Ⓑ	Ⓒ	Ⓓ

Lesson 3-8   Name _____

---

1 Count on by 2.

20, 22, 24, _____

21   25   26   28
Ⓐ   Ⓑ   Ⓒ   Ⓓ

---

2 Adam counted on by _____. He skip counted by _____.

15, 20, 25, 30

15   10   5   2
Ⓐ   Ⓑ   Ⓒ   Ⓓ

---

3 What number is next?

18, 15, 12, _____

11   9   6   3
Ⓐ   Ⓑ   Ⓒ   Ⓓ

---

4 There are 3 spiders. How many legs in all?

8, 16, _____

3   18   20   24
Ⓐ   Ⓑ   Ⓒ   Ⓓ

---

5 There are 4 pairs of socks in the drawer. How many socks in all?

12   8   4   1
Ⓐ   Ⓑ   Ⓒ   Ⓓ

Lesson 3-9   Name _____

1 Which number is <u>even</u>?

3   5   7   8
Ⓐ   Ⓑ   Ⓒ   Ⓓ

---

2 Which sum is <u>even</u>?

$3 + 2 = 5$ $8 + 4 = 12$ $6 + 3 = 9$ $7 + 4 = 11$
   Ⓐ   Ⓑ   Ⓒ   Ⓓ

---

3 What is the next <u>odd</u> number after 37?

35	36	37	38	39	40
	46	47	48	49	50
			58		

35   38   39   47
Ⓐ   Ⓑ   Ⓒ   Ⓓ

---

4 Which is a group of all <u>odd</u> numbers?

1, 2, 4   5, 7, 8   6, 9, 12   5, 7, 9
   Ⓐ   Ⓑ   Ⓒ   Ⓓ

---

5 Katie started to count with 11. She skip counted by 2. Did she count <u>even</u> or <u>odd</u> numbers? How do you know?

11, _____, _____, _____

_____

33

Lesson 3-10   Name _____

1 What is the fifth letter? T E N N E S S E E

N   S   E   T
Ⓐ   Ⓑ   Ⓒ   Ⓓ

2 Which statement is true? | TENNESSEE |

Ⓐ The second, fifth and eighth letters are the same.

Ⓑ The third letter is e.

Ⓒ The sixth letter is e.

Ⓓ The first and eighth letters are vowels.

3 Which animal is third in line from the barn?

horse   cow   pig   sheep duck rabbit

Ⓐ cow
Ⓑ pig
Ⓒ horse
Ⓓ sheep

4 Which car is second in line to buy gas?

Ⓐ   Ⓑ   Ⓒ   Ⓓ

5 There are 15 people in line to buy tickets for Tennessee Historical Society. How many are in line before the eleventh person?

1 0   1 1   1 2   1 3
Ⓐ   Ⓑ   Ⓒ   Ⓓ

34

Lesson 3-11   Name _____

Use the chart for
1–2 to find the
numbers.

51	52	53	54	55	56	57	58	59	60
61	62	63	64	65	66	67	68	69	70

1 It is less than 60. It is greater than 56. It is an <u>even</u> number.

56   57   58   59
Ⓐ   Ⓑ   Ⓒ   Ⓓ

2 It is greater than 59. It has a 3 for the ones digit. It is less than 69.

33   53   55   63
Ⓐ   Ⓑ   Ⓒ   Ⓓ

Use the chart for 3–4.

Name	Height
Chad	45 inches
Drake	51 inches
Danielle	53 inches

3 Which child's height is greater than 52 inches?

Chad   Drake   Danielle   None of the children
Ⓐ   Ⓑ   Ⓒ   Ⓓ

4 Which child's height has a 5 in the ones place?

Chad   Drake   Danielle   None of the children
Ⓐ   Ⓑ   Ⓒ   Ⓓ

5 The number has an <u>even</u> number in the tens place.
Which number could <u>not</u> be the number?

45   53   65   88
Ⓐ   Ⓑ   Ⓒ   Ⓓ

© Pearson Education, Inc. 2

35

Lesson 3-12   Name _____

1 What is the total amount
of money?

  5¢   26¢   27¢   50¢
  Ⓐ   Ⓑ   Ⓒ   Ⓓ

---

2 You have 4 coins that total 31¢. Which coins do you have?

  Ⓐ 3 dimes

  Ⓑ 1 dime, 3 pennies

  Ⓒ 1 dime, 2 nickels, 1 penny

  Ⓓ 3 dimes, 1 penny

---

3 Maria has 3 dimes and 1 nickel. How much money does
Maria have in all?

  35¢   31¢   20¢   4¢
  Ⓐ   Ⓑ   Ⓒ   Ⓓ

---

4 Inside Erin's purse is 17¢. What is the fewest number of
coins in her purse? Hint: Circle the coins that make 17¢.

  Ⓐ 7

  Ⓑ 6

  Ⓒ 5

  Ⓓ 4

---

5 Would you rather have 5 nickels or 3 dimes to spend? Explain.

_____

Lesson 3-13   Name _____

---

1 What is the total amount of money?

50¢   40¢   20¢   10¢
Ⓐ   Ⓑ   Ⓒ   Ⓓ

---

2 Which group of coins is 75¢?

Ⓐ 1 half-dollar

Ⓑ 1 half-dollar, 1 quarter

Ⓒ 1 quarter

Ⓓ 3 half-dollars

---

3 Which coin has the <u>greatest</u> value?

Ⓐ   Ⓑ   Ⓒ   Ⓓ

---

4 A dime is added to 53¢. How much money is there in all?

54¢   58¢   59¢   63¢
Ⓐ   Ⓑ   Ⓒ   Ⓓ

---

5 Nathan put 2 quarters and 1 half-dollar in his piggy bank. How much money did he put in?

150¢   100¢   40¢   4¢
Ⓐ   Ⓑ   Ⓒ   Ⓓ

Lesson 3-14   Name _____

1 What is the total amount of money?

Ⓐ 52¢

Ⓑ 62¢

Ⓒ 67¢

Ⓓ 72¢

---

2 What amount is the same as 2 dimes and 1 nickel?

1 half-dollar	1 quarter	1 quarter, 1 nickel	4 nickels
Ⓐ	Ⓑ	Ⓒ	Ⓓ

---

3 Which coins are needed to buy the popcorn?

Ⓐ 1 quarter, 2 dimes

Ⓑ 2 quarters

Ⓒ 4 dimes

Ⓓ 5 nickels

---

4 Which symbol makes a true statement? 35¢ ◯ 35¢

>	<	=	$
Ⓐ	Ⓑ	Ⓒ	Ⓓ

---

5 Ashley has 1 half-dollar and 1 quarter to buy one can of cat food. Which statement is true?

Ⓐ She has exactly the correct amount of money.

Ⓑ She needs 2 more pennies

Ⓒ She has more money than she needs.

Ⓓ She needs 1 more penny.

Lesson 3-15   Name _____

1 Sarah has one coin in her pocket. The money she has is more than 20¢ and less than 50¢. What coin does Sarah have in her pocket?

dime   quarter   half-dollar   nickel
Ⓐ   Ⓑ   Ⓒ   Ⓓ

---

2 What symbol makes the statement true?

+   <   =   >
Ⓐ   Ⓑ   Ⓒ   Ⓓ

---

3 What has the same value as 1 quarter, 1 nickel, and 2 pennies?

Ⓐ 3 dimes, 2 pennies

Ⓑ 2 dimes, 1 nickel, 1 penny

Ⓒ 1 half-dollar

Ⓓ 2 dimes, 3 pennies

---

4 You have 3 coins in your pocket. There is 1 nickel and 1 half-dollar. If the total is 65¢, what is the third coin?

nickel   dime   quarter   half-dollar
Ⓐ   Ⓑ   Ⓒ   Ⓓ

---

5 Draw some coins that have a value of more than 51¢ and less than 99¢.

39

Lesson 3-16   Name _____

1 Which group of coins does <u>not</u> equal 50¢?

   Ⓐ I quarter, 2 dimes, I nickel

   Ⓑ 5 dimes

   Ⓒ 2 quarters, I nickel

   Ⓓ I half-dollar

2 Which group of coins does <u>not</u> equal 77¢?

   Ⓐ 2 quarters, 2 dimes, I nickel

   Ⓑ I half-dollar, I quarter, 2 pennies

   Ⓒ 3 quarters, 2 pennies

   Ⓓ 7 dimes, I nickel, 2 pennies

---

3 What is the <u>least</u> number of coins needed to make 27¢?

   2   3   4   5

   Ⓐ   Ⓑ   Ⓒ   Ⓓ

---

4 Dave has 75¢. Which 3 coins make 75¢?

   Ⓐ I nickel   Ⓒ 3 quarters

   Ⓑ I half-dollar, I quarter   Ⓓ 2 half-dollars

---

5 Show the 30¢ in different ways. Record the coins with tally marks.

Quarter	Dime	Nickel	Total
I		I	30¢

Lesson 3-17   Name _____

1 Mrs. Chin buys an ice cream cone for 49¢. She pays with 1 half-dollar. How much is Mrs. Chin's change?

1¢	2¢	5¢	10¢
Ⓐ	Ⓑ	Ⓒ	Ⓓ

2 Liza buys a notebook for 66¢. She pays with 70¢. How much is Liza's change?

10¢	7¢	5¢	4¢
Ⓐ	Ⓑ	Ⓒ	Ⓓ

3 A ticket to ride the rollercoaster is 65¢. Jim pays for his ticket with 3 quarters. Which group of coins could not be his change?

Ⓐ 1 dime

Ⓑ 2 nickels

Ⓒ 2 dimes

Ⓓ 1 nickel and 5 pennies

4 Shellie wants to buy a doll that costs 92¢. She pays with 1 dollar. Which group of coins is her change?

Ⓐ 9 pennies

Ⓑ 1 dime and 2 pennies

Ⓒ 1 nickel and 3 pennies

Ⓓ 1 dime

5 Ramon buys a birthday card for 35¢. He pays with 2 quarters. What is his change?

15¢	13¢	10¢	5¢
Ⓐ	Ⓑ	Ⓒ	Ⓓ

Lesson 3-18   Name _____

1 How many quarters are in 1 dollar?

3   4   5   10
Ⓐ   Ⓑ   Ⓒ   Ⓓ

---

2 Which symbol makes a true statement?

Ⓐ <
Ⓑ =
Ⓒ >
Ⓓ ?

_____¢   ◯   _____¢

---

3 Which group of coins makes $1.00?

Ⓐ 3 quarters, 2 dimes, 1 nickel

Ⓑ 1 half-dollar, 1 quarter

Ⓒ 3 quarters, 2 dimes

Ⓓ 1 half-dollar, 3 quarters

---

4 What 2 additional coins are needed to make $1.00?

Ⓐ 2 quarters

Ⓑ 1 half-dollar

Ⓒ 2 dimes

Ⓓ 1 dime and 1 nickel

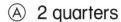

---

5 Would you rather have 20 nickels or 10 dimes? Explain?

Lesson 3-19   Name _____

1 Count on to find the total amount of money.

52¢	57¢	62¢	77¢
Ⓐ	Ⓑ	Ⓒ	Ⓓ

---

2 Andy has saved 75¢. He will earn a $1.00 for cleaning his room. After Andy cleans his room, how much will Andy have in all?

$1.75	$1.50	$1.00	75¢
Ⓐ	Ⓑ	Ⓒ	Ⓓ

---

3 How much more money is needed to make $5.00?

$1.00	$2.00	$3.00	$5.00
Ⓐ	Ⓑ	Ⓒ	Ⓓ

---

4 What is the total amount of money?

Ⓐ $4.00

Ⓑ $4.60

Ⓒ $4.75

Ⓓ $5.60

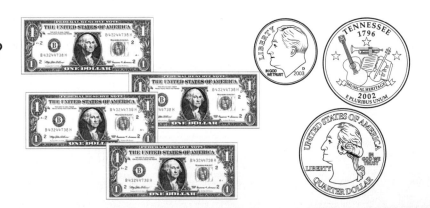

Lesson 4-1   Name _____

1 Which shows the answer to the problem?

37   +   40   =

37	47	77	87
Ⓐ	Ⓑ	Ⓒ	Ⓓ

---

2 Solve:

30 + 64 =

94	84	44	34
Ⓐ	Ⓑ	Ⓒ	Ⓓ

3 Which number makes the number sentence true?

20 + _____ = 42

4	12	22	42
Ⓐ	Ⓑ	Ⓒ	Ⓓ

---

4 Solve: 13 + 20 =

Ⓐ 40

Ⓑ 33

Ⓒ 30

Ⓓ 23

5 Solve: 50 + 26 =

Ⓐ 36

Ⓑ 50

Ⓒ 70

Ⓓ 76

Lesson 4-2   Name _____

1 Solve:

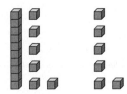

16 + 6 =

12	21	22	32
Ⓐ	Ⓑ	Ⓒ	Ⓓ

2 Solve:

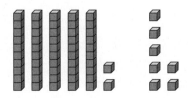

52 + 7 =

57	59	64	69
Ⓐ	Ⓑ	Ⓒ	Ⓓ

---

3 At Reelfoot Lake, Amy and Aisha saw 43 turtles. Jake saw 8 turtles. How many turtles did they see in all?

49	50	51	53
Ⓐ	Ⓑ	Ⓒ	Ⓓ

---

4 How many students are there in all in Mrs. Jones's class?

20	28	30	33
Ⓐ	Ⓑ	Ⓒ	Ⓓ

Students in
Mrs. Jones's Class

Girls	11
Boys	9

---

5 Shawn plants 3 rows of carrots. Each row has 10 carrots. He wants to plant 12 more carrots. How many carrots will Shawn have planted in all? Draw a picture of his garden.

_____ carrots

Lesson 4-3   Name _____

1 Which is the answer to the problem?

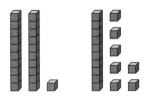

21 + 17 =

Ⓐ 36
Ⓑ 38
Ⓒ 46
Ⓓ 49

---

2 Solve:

Ⓐ 11
Ⓑ 55
Ⓒ 56
Ⓓ 61

35 + 26 =

---

3 Solve:

67 + _____ =

Ⓐ 95
Ⓑ 91
Ⓒ 85
Ⓓ 81

---

4 The table shows where visitors to Nashville came from.

Visitors to Nashville	
Murfreesboro	43
Franklin	52
Pegram	29

How many visitors came from Franklin and Pegram in all?

67   81   90   95
Ⓐ   Ⓑ   Ⓒ   Ⓓ

---

5 Kevin spent 70¢ at the store. Which things did he buy?

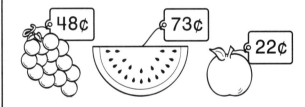

48¢   73¢   22¢

Ⓐ watermelon and apple
Ⓑ grapes and watermelon
Ⓒ apple and grapes
Ⓓ watermelon

Lesson 4-4   Name _____

1 Julia has 80¢. She wants to buy a pen for 32¢. Which other item can she buy?

 74¢
Ⓐ

 45¢
Ⓑ

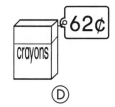 80¢
Ⓒ

crayons 62¢
Ⓓ

---

2 Eric has 40¢. Which two items can he buy?

 Pasta 41¢

 SOUP 23¢

 Tuna 35¢

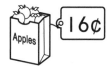 Apples 16¢

soup, apples   apples, tuna   pasta, soup   tuna, pasta
Ⓐ   Ⓑ   Ⓒ   Ⓓ

---

3 It will cost 56¢ for Tina to send a letter. Which two stamps should she buy?

Ⓐ

Ⓑ

Ⓒ

Ⓓ

---

4 Darius has 60¢. Which two things can he buy?

Ⓐ banana, pizza

Ⓑ popcorn, muffin

Ⓒ banana, muffin

Ⓓ pizza, popcorn

Food		Price
Popcorn	🍿	45¢
Muffin	🧁	30¢
Banana	🍌	25¢
Pizza	🍕	40¢

Lesson 4-5   Name _____

1 Which is the answer to the problem?

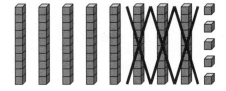

85 − 30 =

55	50	45	40
Ⓐ	Ⓑ	Ⓒ	Ⓓ

2 Solve:

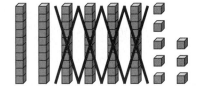

68 − 40 =

20	28	30	58
Ⓐ	Ⓑ	Ⓒ	Ⓓ

3 Solve:

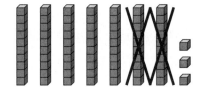

73 − 20 =

50	53	90	93
Ⓐ	Ⓑ	Ⓒ	Ⓓ

4 Lee bought a postcard of the Great Smoky Mountains for 60¢. He gave the clerk 75¢. How much change did he get back?

Ⓐ 10¢

Ⓑ 11¢

Ⓒ 15¢

Ⓓ 18¢

5 Shari picked 10 flowers in the garden. Ying picked 34 flowers. How many more flowers did Ying pick?

Ⓐ 10

Ⓑ 14

Ⓒ 20

Ⓓ 24

Lesson 4-6   Name _____

1 Solve:

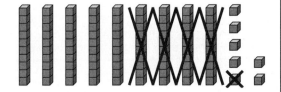

97 − 41 =

55	56	57	58
Ⓐ	Ⓑ	Ⓒ	Ⓓ

2 Solve:

66 − 32 =

38	34	28	22
Ⓐ	Ⓑ	Ⓒ	Ⓓ

3 Solve:

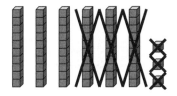

63 − 33 =

11	20	30	33
Ⓐ	Ⓑ	Ⓒ	Ⓓ

4 Jack had 85¢. He let Lin borrow these coins. How much money does Jack have left?

82¢	65¢	50¢	30¢
Ⓐ	Ⓑ	Ⓒ	Ⓓ

5 Tony bought 45 postcards in Memphis to send to his friends. On Monday, he sent 13 postcards. On Tuesday, he sent 10 more. How many postcards does Tony have left? Tell how you found the answer.

_____ postcards

Lesson 4-7   Name _____

1 Jason had 90¢. He spent this much.

About how much money does he have left?

70¢   60¢   50¢   40¢
Ⓐ   Ⓑ   Ⓒ   Ⓓ

2 Kelly had 80¢. She bought a book and had 32¢ left.
About how much did the book cost?

70¢   60¢   50¢   40¢
Ⓐ   Ⓑ   Ⓒ   Ⓓ

3 John invited 50 people to his party. There were 38 people at the party. About how many people did not come?

10   20   30   40
Ⓐ   Ⓑ   Ⓒ   Ⓓ

4 There are 70 seats in the movie theater. 42 people come in to watch the movie. About how many seats are empty.

10   20   30   40
Ⓐ   Ⓑ   Ⓒ   Ⓓ

5 Estimate. Which of the following has a difference of less than 30?

Ⓐ 90 − 58

Ⓑ 70 − 33

Ⓒ 60 − 22

Ⓓ 50 − 28

6 Estimate. Which of the following has a difference of about 50?

Ⓐ 72 − 20

Ⓑ 67 − 30

Ⓒ 84 − 40

Ⓓ 93 − 50

Lesson 4-8   Name _____

1 Patrick spent exactly 90¢ on two postcards. Which two did he buy?

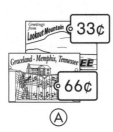
33¢
66¢
Ⓐ

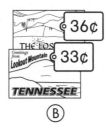
36¢
33¢
Ⓑ

66¢
54¢
Ⓒ

54¢
36¢
Ⓓ

---

2 Which two numbers have a sum of 80?

| 22 | 36 | 45 | 58 |

Ⓐ 36 , 45

Ⓑ 22 , 58

Ⓒ 36 , 58

Ⓓ 22 , 45

3 Which two numbers have a sum of 50?

| 16 | 28 | 34 | 42 |

Ⓐ 16 , 34

Ⓑ 28 , 42

Ⓒ 16 , 42

Ⓓ 28 , 34

---

4 Which number makes the following true?

$37 + \boxed{} = 60$

Ⓐ 33

Ⓑ 27

Ⓒ 23

Ⓓ 17

5 Which number makes the following true?

$21 + \boxed{} = 40$

Ⓐ 19

Ⓑ 20

Ⓒ 29

Ⓓ 30

Lesson 4-9   Name _____

---

1   What is the pattern?
32, 29, 26, 23, 20, 17, 14

add 3   add 5   subtract 3   subtract 4
Ⓐ   Ⓑ   Ⓒ   Ⓓ

---

2   Which number completes the pattern?
91, 82, 73, 64, _____, 46, 37

55   57   60   62
Ⓐ   Ⓑ   Ⓒ   Ⓓ

---

3   Which numbers complete the pattern?
47, 53, 59, 65, 71, 77, _____, _____, _____

79, 83, 85   81, 87, 95   83, 89, 95   85, 91, 97
Ⓐ   Ⓑ   Ⓒ   Ⓓ

---

4   Ms. Cane's class recorded the number of books they sold.

Day	Monday	Tuesday	Wednesday	Thursday	Friday
Books Sold	44	48	52	56	?

Look at the pattern. How many books were sold Friday?

58   60   62   64
Ⓐ   Ⓑ   Ⓒ   Ⓓ

---

5   Describe the pattern. Then draw the next group in the pattern.

☆△△△☆☆☆☆☆△△△△△△☆☆☆☆☆☆☆☆☆

Lesson 4-10   Name _____

1 Marcel wants to buy a Graceland pen for 35¢.
Which group of coins does he need?

Ⓐ

Ⓑ

Ⓒ

Ⓓ

---

2 Which number makes the
following true?

$$40 + \square = 100$$

45	50	55	60
Ⓐ	Ⓑ	Ⓒ	Ⓓ

3 Which number makes the
following true?

$$75 + \square = 100$$

45	35	25	15
Ⓐ	Ⓑ	Ⓒ	Ⓓ

---

4 **Solve:**   If $80 + 20 = 100$,
then $100 - 80 =$

10	20	25	30
Ⓐ	Ⓑ	Ⓒ	Ⓓ

5 **Solve:**   If $70 + 30 = 100$,
then $100 - 30 =$

75	70	65	60
Ⓐ	Ⓑ	Ⓒ	Ⓓ

Accomplishments *2.1.3.a. Solve story problems involving numbers to 100.
*2.1.3.b. Check for the reasonableness of solutions.

Lesson 4-11   Name _____

---

1 Diane had 88 beads. She made a necklace. There were
16 beads left. How many beads were on the necklace?

68   72   82   88
Ⓐ   Ⓑ   Ⓒ   Ⓓ

---

2 Ron delivered 14 newspapers. Then he delivered
11 more. How many newspapers did Ron deliver?

25   14   5   3
Ⓐ   Ⓑ   Ⓒ   Ⓓ

---

3 There were 27 ducks in the pond. Then 12 flew away.
How many ducks are left?

39   35   26   15
Ⓐ   Ⓑ   Ⓒ   Ⓓ

---

4 Melissa has 22 crayons. John has 45 crayons.
How many crayons do they have in all?

23   27   67   83
Ⓐ   Ⓑ   Ⓒ   Ⓓ

---

5 Louis had 28 pairs of socks. Then he lost some in the
wash. How many pairs of socks could he have now?

30 pairs   28 pairs   19 pairs

Tell why you chose your answer.

Accomplishments 2.1.1.c. Read and write numerals to 999. ***2.1.1.j.** Order whole numbers less than 1000.
*2.1.3.d. Add and subtract efficiently and accurately with single-digit numbers.
*2.1.3.e. Use a variety of strategies and representations to add and subtract two-digit whole numbers.

Lesson 4-12   Name _____

1 Theresa wants to buy a postcard of
Nashville for 18¢. She has 9¢.
How much more money does she need?

18¢

Nashville

8¢	9¢	10¢	11¢
Ⓐ	Ⓑ	Ⓒ	Ⓓ

---

2 **Solve:**   43 − 20 =

17	23	27	63
Ⓐ	Ⓑ	Ⓒ	Ⓓ

3 **Solve:**   99 − 35 =

55	64	65	74
Ⓐ	Ⓑ	Ⓒ	Ⓓ

---

4 Which is the standard form
for thirty-five?

Ⓐ   35

Ⓑ 305

Ⓒ   53

Ⓓ 503

5 The table shows how many
books Mr. Lee sold in his store.

Science books	Comic books	Art books
7	34	10

How many comic books and art
books did Mr. Lee sell in all?

23	40	41	44
Ⓐ	Ⓑ	Ⓒ	Ⓓ

---

6 **Solve:**   40 + 16 =

36	46	50	56
Ⓐ	Ⓑ	Ⓒ	Ⓓ

7 When 19, 58, 45, and 23 are
ordered from greatest to least,
which number is last?

58	45	23	19
Ⓐ	Ⓑ	Ⓒ	Ⓓ

Lesson 5-1   Name _____

1 For which number expression do you need to regroup to add?

- Ⓐ $85 + 6$
- Ⓑ $43 + 5$
- Ⓒ $64 + 4$
- Ⓓ $56 + 3$

2 Solve:

$$38 \quad + 7 =$$

31	35	41	45
Ⓐ	Ⓑ	Ⓒ	Ⓓ

---

3 Solve: $24 + 8 =$ _____

Ⓐ   Ⓑ   Ⓒ   Ⓓ

---

4 Which one digit number can be added to 27 without having to regroup?

2	4	5	7
Ⓐ	Ⓑ	Ⓒ	Ⓓ

---

5 Mike is putting away his crayons.
He puts 10 in each box.
He has 3 full boxes and 4 extra crayons.
He finds 7 more crayons.
How many full boxes will Mike have?
Explain how you found the answer.

_____ boxes of crayons

Lesson 5-2   Name _____

1 Solve: 54
                 + 7

Tens	Ones
□	
5	4
+	7

Ⓐ 51
Ⓑ 61
Ⓒ 63
Ⓓ 73

2 Solve: 35
                 + 3

Tens	Ones
3	5
+	3

Ⓐ 65
Ⓑ 48
Ⓒ 42
Ⓓ 38

3 Solve:

28
+ 9

47   37   21   18
Ⓐ   Ⓑ   Ⓒ   Ⓓ

4 Solve:

57
+ 3

54   59   60   70
Ⓐ   Ⓑ   Ⓒ   Ⓓ

5 Solve:

49
+ 2

57   51   47   37
Ⓐ   Ⓑ   Ⓒ   Ⓓ

6 Solve:

18
+ 5

23   22   13   3
Ⓐ   Ⓑ   Ⓒ   Ⓓ

7 In which problem do you need to regroup to add?

17	22	43	66
+ 5	+ 6	+ 4	+ 3
22	28	47	69
Ⓐ	Ⓑ	Ⓒ	Ⓓ

Lesson 5-3   Name _____

1 Solve: 23
                  + 19

Tens	Ones
2	3
+ 1	9

Ⓐ 16

Ⓑ 32

Ⓒ 36

Ⓓ 42

2 Solve: 55
                  + 34

Tens	Ones
5	5
+ 3	4

Ⓐ 99

Ⓑ 89

Ⓒ 81

Ⓓ 21

---

3 In which problem do you need to regroup to add?

       35   53   44   68
     + 43   + 16   + 28   + 31
     ─────   ─────   ─────   ─────
       78   69   72   99
       Ⓐ   Ⓑ   Ⓒ   Ⓓ

---

4 Kevin has a coin jar. There are 35 coins in the jar. He adds 35 more coins. How many coins are in the jar now?

70   75   80   90
Ⓐ   Ⓑ   Ⓒ   Ⓓ

---

5 Matt and Maria are taking pictures of Memphis. They have taken 45 pictures in all. Which numbers show how many each could have taken?

Ⓐ 39 and 16

Ⓑ 22 and 26

Ⓒ 28 and 17

Ⓓ 33 and 18

Lesson 5-4   Name _____

1 **Solve:**   46 + 27 = _____

    Ⓐ 21

    Ⓑ 61

    Ⓒ 63

    Ⓓ 73

2 **Solve:**   38¢ + 24¢ = _____

    Ⓐ 52¢

    Ⓑ 54¢

    Ⓒ 62¢

    Ⓓ 72¢

3 There are 56 children from Nashville at the play. There are 33 children from Knoxville at the play. How many children are from Nashville and Knoxville in all?

56 + 33 =

99	96	89	83
Ⓐ	Ⓑ	Ⓒ	Ⓓ

4 Alex collected 18 shells.
Andy collected 23 shells.
How many shells did they collect in all?

31	35	41	46
Ⓐ	Ⓑ	Ⓒ	Ⓓ

5 Jesse has 34 books. Tamara has 49 books.
How many books do they have in all?
Write the addition problem. Find the sum.

_____ books

Lesson 5-5   Name _____

Use this table for 1 and 2.

Food	Pizza	Sandwich	Muffin	Banana
Price	53¢	38¢	47¢	25¢

1 Ian has 85¢. Which items does he have the exact amount to buy?

- Ⓐ
- Ⓑ
- Ⓒ
- Ⓓ

2 Nina has 23¢. Jake has 27¢. They put their money together. Which item can they __not__ buy?

- Ⓐ pizza
- Ⓑ sandwich
- Ⓒ muffin
- Ⓓ banana

3 Solve:

71¢
+ 8¢

77¢	79¢	83¢	87¢
Ⓐ	Ⓑ	Ⓒ	Ⓓ

4 Solve:

37¢
+ 24¢

51¢	53¢	61¢	63¢
Ⓐ	Ⓑ	Ⓒ	Ⓓ

5 Mia has 45¢. Then she finds these coins.
Which item does Mia have the exact amount for?

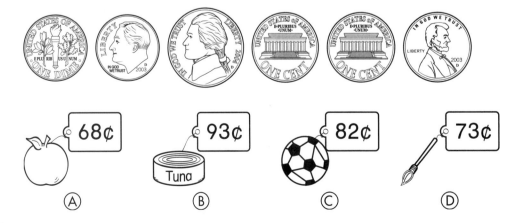

68¢	93¢	82¢	73¢
Ⓐ	Ⓑ	Ⓒ	Ⓓ

Lesson 5-6   Name _____

1 Solve: 14
                 21
               + 8

ⓐ 43

ⓑ 39

ⓒ 38

ⓓ 27

2 Solve: 18
                 32
               + 14

ⓐ 46

ⓑ 54

ⓒ 64

ⓓ 66

3 The chart shows how many books each student got at the library. How many books did they get in all?

Mark	15
Kim	26
Daren	21

45   50   57   62
ⓐ   ⓑ   ⓒ   ⓓ

4 Kate had 33 stickers. She bought 25 more stickers. She found 17 stickers. How many stickers does Kate have in all?

33 + 25 + 17 = _____

58   60   75   80
ⓐ   ⓑ   ⓒ   ⓓ

5 On Friday, 23 people visited the Grand Ole Opry. On Saturday, 34 people came. On Sunday, 23 people came. How many people came in all?

46   57   70   80
ⓐ   ⓑ   ⓒ   ⓓ

Accomplishments *2.1.3.a. Solve story problems involving numbers to 100.
*2.1.3.e. Use a variety of strategies and representations to add … two-digit whole numbers.
2.5.1.d. Read and interpret tables….

Lesson 5-7   Name _____

1 How many crayons and pens does Mr. Ray's art class have?

Crayons	36
Markers	22
Pens	53

40   58   83   89
Ⓐ   Ⓑ   Ⓒ   Ⓓ

2 From this chart, children ate how many apples and bananas?

🍉	🍌	🧁	🍎
15	28	31	44

59   64   72   75
Ⓐ   Ⓑ   Ⓒ   Ⓓ

The chart shows how many cans each child collected on each day. Use this chart for 3–5.

Student	Monday	Tuesday	Wednesday	Thursday	Friday
Ryan	12	19	24	26	15
Darren	16	21	33	37	26
Lisa	21	27	34	29	22

3 How many cans did the children collect in all on Tuesday?

40   46   47   67
Ⓐ   Ⓑ   Ⓒ   Ⓓ

4 How many cans did Ryan collect on Monday, Tuesday, and Wednesday?

65   59   55   46
Ⓐ   Ⓑ   Ⓒ   Ⓓ

5 How many cans were collected each day? _____

On which day were the most cans collected? _____

Lesson 5-8   Name _____

1 What numbers would you use to estimate the sum
of 77 + 23?

70	80	70	80
+ 20	+ 30	+ 30	+ 20
Ⓐ	Ⓑ	Ⓒ	Ⓓ

2 What numbers would you use to estimate the sum
of 32 + 58?

30	40	30	40
+ 50	+ 60	+ 60	+ 50
Ⓐ	Ⓑ	Ⓒ	Ⓓ

3 There are 41 dogwood trees around the school. There
are 26 more trees around the playground. About how
many trees are there in all?

80	70	60	50
Ⓐ	Ⓑ	Ⓒ	Ⓓ

4 72 + 18 is about _____.

90	80	70	60
Ⓐ	Ⓑ	Ⓒ	Ⓓ

5 Jim has 18 marbles. Kara has 22 marbles. About how
many marbles do they have in all?

20	30	40	50
Ⓐ	Ⓑ	Ⓒ	Ⓓ

Lesson 5-9   Name _____

1 Chris bought two stamps for 60¢. Which two stamps did he buy?

ⓐ   ⓑ   ©   ⓓ

2 Solve:

19   +   _____   =

56   65   75   94
ⓐ   ⓑ   ©   ⓓ

3 Ms. Howe drove 33 miles from Manchester to Murfreesboro. She drove 31 miles from Murfreesboro to Nashville. How many miles did she drive in all?

64   62   46   32
ⓐ   ⓑ   ©   ⓓ

4 Jenna has 12 tomato plants and 37 bean plants. About how many plants does she have in all?

20   30   40   50
ⓐ   ⓑ   ©   ⓓ

5 Each case holds 10 CDs. There are 3 cases of jazz music and 2 cases of guitar music. There are also 4 CDs of piano music. How many CDs are there in all? Explain.

_____ CDs

Lesson 5-10   Name _____

1 Delia has 64 flowers. Which two kinds of flowers does she have?

  Ⓐ 12 tulips and 42 daffodils

  Ⓑ 24 violets and 30 lilies

  Ⓒ 28 marigolds and 36 roses

  Ⓓ 32 pansies and 38 daisies

2 There are 46 birds in a tree. Which two kinds of birds are in the tree?

  Ⓐ 22 ravens, 34 crows

  Ⓑ 26 finches, 30 sparrows

  Ⓒ 31 cardinals, 15 doves

  Ⓓ 38 canaries, 14 robins

3 Mr. Cheng sold 58 vegetables at his stand. He sold only two kinds of vegetables. Which kinds were they?

Vegetable	Tomatoes	Beans	Carrots	Radishes
Amount Sold	35	16	23	24

  Ⓐ carrots and tomatoes

  Ⓑ radishes and carrots

  Ⓒ tomatoes and beans

  Ⓓ beans and radishes

4 Jeff paid 83¢ for two stamps. Which two stamps did he buy?

Ⓐ

Ⓑ

Ⓒ

Ⓓ

5 Rosie spent 77¢ at the store. Which two things did she buy?

Ⓐ 45¢ 23¢

Ⓑ 23¢ 50¢

Ⓒ 50¢ 32¢

Ⓓ 45¢ 32¢

Accomplishments *2.1.3.d. Add and subtract efficiently and accurately with single-digit numbers. **2.1.3.e.** Use a variety of strategies and representations to add … two-digit whole numbers.

Lesson 5-11   Name _____

1 Duane bought 8 bags of peanuts. Tracy bought 7 bags.
How many bags of peanuts did they buy in all?

11	15	16	18
Ⓐ	Ⓑ	Ⓒ	Ⓓ

2 Ginny picked 2 bags of apples. Each bag held 10 apples.
Pa picked 4 apples. How many apples do they have in all?

	20	18	16
Ⓐ	Ⓑ	Ⓒ	Ⓓ

3 Rob had 38 bugs in his collection. Then he found
14 more bugs. How many bugs does he have in all?

24	40	44	52
Ⓐ	Ⓑ	Ⓒ	Ⓓ

The chart shows how many horses the children in Mr. Hall's class saw
each day at the farm. Use the chart for 4–5.

Monday	Tuesday	Wednesday	Thursday	Friday
13	6	7	11	5

4 How many horses did they see on Monday and Friday?

11	12	18	25
Ⓐ	Ⓑ	Ⓒ	Ⓓ

5 How many horses did the children see in all?

37	41	42	43
Ⓐ	Ⓑ	Ⓒ	Ⓓ

Lesson 6-1   Name _____

1 For which number expression do you need to regroup to subtract?

Ⓐ $27 - 5$

Ⓑ $24 - 4$

Ⓒ $18 - 7$

Ⓓ $15 - 6$

2 Solve: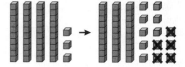

$$43 - 5 =$$

32   38   42   48
Ⓐ   Ⓑ   Ⓒ   Ⓓ

---

3 Solve: $25 - 6 =$ _____

Ⓐ   Ⓑ   Ⓒ   Ⓓ

---

4 Solve: $54 - 8 =$ _____

62   56   54   46
Ⓐ   Ⓑ   Ⓒ   Ⓓ

---

5 Solve: $31 - 7 =$ _____

24   28   36   38
Ⓐ   Ⓑ   Ⓒ   Ⓓ

---

6 There were 12 ducks swimming in the Tennessee River. 5 ducks flew away. How many ducks were left in the river?

17   13   8   7
Ⓐ   Ⓑ   Ⓒ   Ⓓ

Lesson 6-2   Name _____

---

1 Solve: 49
                   − 6

    33   40   43   55
    Ⓐ   Ⓑ   Ⓒ   Ⓓ

2 Solve: 56
                   − 8

    52   48   46   44
    Ⓐ   Ⓑ   Ⓒ   Ⓓ

3 Solve: 82
                   − 7

    65   75   85   89
    Ⓐ   Ⓑ   Ⓒ   Ⓓ

4 Solve: 65
                   − 4

    51   59   61   69
    Ⓐ   Ⓑ   Ⓒ   Ⓓ

---

5 There are 33 people on the bus. 7 people get off. How
many people are left on the bus?

    40   34   26   24
    Ⓐ   Ⓑ   Ⓒ   Ⓓ

---

6 Tammy put 18 shells down on the beach.
This many washed away.

How many shells does Tammy have left?

    13   15   20   23
    Ⓐ   Ⓑ   Ⓒ   Ⓓ

---

7 There were 44 cardinals in the tree. 9 cardinals
flew away. How many cardinals were left in the tree?
Write the subtraction sentence.

_____ − _____ = _____   _____ cardinals

68

Lesson 6-3   Name _____

1 Solve: 18
                  − 11

   7   9   12   17
   Ⓐ   Ⓑ   Ⓒ   Ⓓ

2 Solve: 43
                  − 24

   11   19   21   27
   Ⓐ   Ⓑ   Ⓒ   Ⓓ

3 In which problem do you need to regroup to subtract?

66	37	49	55
− 30	− 21	− 28	− 37
36	16	21	18
Ⓐ	Ⓑ	Ⓒ	Ⓓ

4 Solve:

$$63 - 29 =$$

    Ⓐ   Ⓑ   Ⓒ   Ⓓ

5 65 children visited Dollywood. 38 children rode the
Thunderhead. 27 children rode the Tennessee Tornado.
Which shows how many more children rode the
Thunderhead than the Tennessee Tornado?

65	27	38	65
− 38	+ 38	− 27	+ 27
33	65	11	92
Ⓐ	Ⓑ	Ⓒ	Ⓓ

Lesson 6-4   Name _____

1 Solve: 87
                 − 54

    Ⓐ 21

    Ⓑ 23

    Ⓒ 31

    Ⓓ 33

2 Solve: 72
                 − 47

    Ⓐ 39

    Ⓑ 34

    Ⓒ 25

    Ⓓ 21

---

3 Ravi scored 34 points in the basketball game. Jimmy scored 18 points in the game. How many more points did Ravi score than Jimmy?

14	16	22	24
Ⓐ	Ⓑ	Ⓒ	Ⓓ

---

4 How much more does the marker cost than the paintbrush?

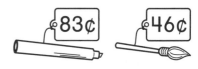

49¢	43¢	37¢	33¢
Ⓐ	Ⓑ	Ⓒ	Ⓓ

---

5 Marcy bought a bag of peanuts. There were 95 peanuts in the bag. Marcy ate this many peanuts.

How many peanuts are left in the bag?

95 − 19 = _____

76	79	84	86
Ⓐ	Ⓑ	Ⓒ	Ⓓ

Lesson 6-5   Name _____

---

1 There were 43 eagles near Reelfoot Lake. 27 eagles flew away. Which number sentence can you use to find how many eagles were left?

Ⓐ $43 + 27 = 70$

Ⓑ $43 + 27 = 64$

Ⓒ $43 - 27 = 26$

Ⓓ $43 - 27 = 16$

---

2 There are 24 monkeys in the Memphis Zoo. There are 13 elephants. Which number sentence tells how many monkeys and elephants in all?

Ⓐ $24 + 13 = 31$

Ⓑ $24 + 13 = 37$

Ⓒ $24 - 13 = 11$

Ⓓ $24 - 13 = 7$

---

3 Pete had 66 baseball cards. He gave 27 cards to Lisa. Which number sentence tells how many cards Pete has left?

Ⓐ $66 + 27 = 93$

Ⓑ $66 + 27 = 81$

Ⓒ $66 - 27 = 39$

Ⓓ $66 - 27 = 41$

---

4 The chart shows the prices of rides at the fair. How much more do you pay to ride the Ferris wheel than the roller coaster? Write a number sentence. Solve it.

Rides	Price
Roller coaster	36¢
Go-carts	83¢
Ferris wheel	58¢

_____¢

Lesson 6-6   Name _____

1 Solve: 88¢
                − 34¢

54¢   52¢   44¢   42¢
Ⓐ   Ⓑ   Ⓒ   Ⓓ

2 Solve: 64¢
                − 27¢

31¢   37¢   43¢   47¢
Ⓐ   Ⓑ   Ⓒ   Ⓓ

3 Solve: 75¢
                − 49¢

36¢   34¢   26¢   24¢
Ⓐ   Ⓑ   Ⓒ   Ⓓ

4 Solve: 55¢
                − 36¢

91¢   21¢   19¢   11¢
Ⓐ   Ⓑ   Ⓒ   Ⓓ

5 Jody has these coins.
She gave her brother 35¢.
How much money does
Jody have left?

57¢   52¢   42¢   37¢
Ⓐ   Ⓑ   Ⓒ   Ⓓ

6 Ben had 93¢. He bought a postcard at The Hermitage.
How much money does Ben have left?

36¢   40¢   44¢   47¢
Ⓐ   Ⓑ   Ⓒ   Ⓓ

7 The chart shows the prices of pies. How much more does an apple pie cost than a cherry pie?

Pie	Apple	Peach	Cherry
Price	71¢	59¢	42¢

33¢   31¢   29¢   23¢
Ⓐ   Ⓑ   Ⓒ   Ⓓ

Lesson 6-7   Name _____

1 What number makes the number sentence true?

$50 - 20 = 10 + \square$

0	10	20	30
Ⓐ	Ⓑ	Ⓒ	Ⓓ

2 What number makes the number sentence true?

$20 + 40 = 90 - \square$

0	10	20	30
Ⓐ	Ⓑ	Ⓒ	Ⓓ

3 What is the best way to check this problem?

```
  37
- 15
----
  20
```

| 37 +15 52 Ⓐ | 22 +15 37 Ⓑ | 37 +22 59 Ⓒ | 22 +15 7 Ⓓ |

4 What is the best way to check this problem?

$56 - 32 = 24$ marbles left.

| 32 +24 56 Ⓐ | 32 -24 8 Ⓑ | 56 +24 80 Ⓒ | 56 +32 88 Ⓓ |

5 81 children at Westside School want to go to the zoo. 58 children want to go to the museum. How many more children want to go to the zoo? Show how you found the answer. Then check your work.

_____ children

Lesson 6-8   Name _____

1 What numbers would you use to estimate 72 − 38?

$$
\begin{array}{c}
70 \\
-\ 30 \\
\hline
\end{array}
\qquad
\begin{array}{c}
80 \\
-\ 30 \\
\hline
\end{array}
\qquad
\begin{array}{c}
70 \\
-\ 40 \\
\hline
\end{array}
\qquad
\begin{array}{c}
80 \\
-\ 40 \\
\hline
\end{array}
$$

Ⓐ   Ⓑ   Ⓒ   Ⓓ

2 What numbers would you use to estimate 46 − 23?

$$
\begin{array}{c}
40 \\
-\ 20 \\
\hline
\end{array}
\qquad
\begin{array}{c}
50 \\
-\ 20 \\
\hline
\end{array}
\qquad
\begin{array}{c}
40 \\
-\ 30 \\
\hline
\end{array}
\qquad
\begin{array}{c}
50 \\
-\ 30 \\
\hline
\end{array}
$$

Ⓐ   Ⓑ   Ⓒ   Ⓓ

3 Kim has 67 marbles. Jose has 31 marbles. About how many more marbles does Kim have than Jose?

20   30   40   50
Ⓐ   Ⓑ   Ⓒ   Ⓓ

4 The chart shows how many children visited Pigeon Forge this week.

Day	Monday	Tuesday	Wednesday	Thursday	Friday
Number of Children	43	61	88	59	27

About how many more children went on Wednesday than on Friday?

60   50   40   30
Ⓐ   Ⓑ   Ⓒ   Ⓓ

5 About how much more does the apple cost than the banana?

50¢   40¢   30¢   20¢
Ⓐ   Ⓑ   Ⓒ   Ⓓ

Accomplishments 2.1.3.c. Use calculators in problem-solving situations. ***2.1.3.e.** Use a variety of strategies and representations to … subtract two-digit whole numbers.

Lesson 6-9   Name _____

1 Solve: 71
          − 46

Ⓐ 25
Ⓑ 35
Ⓒ 27
Ⓓ 37

2 Solve: 84
          − 37

Ⓐ 57
Ⓑ 53
Ⓒ 47
Ⓓ 41

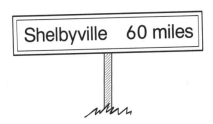

Tens	Ones
8̸	4̸
− 3	7

---

3 Mr. Monroe will drive 60 miles from Nashville to Shelbyville. He drives 27 miles and stops for lunch. How many more miles does he have to drive to get to Shelbyville?

Shelbyville   60 miles

33   37   43   47
Ⓐ   Ⓑ   Ⓒ   Ⓓ

---

4 Julie had 52 markers. She gave 19 markers to Bob. About how many markers does she have left?

20   30   40   50
Ⓐ   Ⓑ   Ⓒ   Ⓓ

---

5 Seth found 4 stacks of books in his attic.
Each stack contained 10 books.
Seth brought 14 books downstairs.
How many books were left in the attic?
Show how you solved the problem.

_____ books left in the attic

Lesson 6-10   Name _____

1 Beth has 5 tulips and 11 roses. Dina has 22 roses. Which shows how many roses there are in all?

Ⓐ 5 + 11

Ⓑ 5 + 22

Ⓒ 11 + 22

Ⓓ 5 + 11 + 22

2 There are 12 potatoes, 24 tomatoes, and 47 beans in the bin. How many more beans than tomatoes are there?

Ⓐ 11

Ⓑ 12

Ⓒ 23

Ⓓ 35

This chart shows how many quarters each child collected.
Use this chart for 3 and 4.

Student	Kelly	Emily	Peter	Robert
Number of quarters	41	28	66	35

3 How many more quarters did Peter collect than Emily?

38	31	25	22
Ⓐ	Ⓑ	Ⓒ	Ⓓ

---

4 Which do you use to find how many quarters Robert and Kelly collected together?

41 + 28	28 + 66	35 + 41	41 + 35
Ⓐ	Ⓑ	Ⓒ	Ⓓ

---

5 How much did Maria spend for one of each kind of pencil?

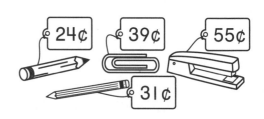

81¢	79¢	63¢	55¢
Ⓐ	Ⓑ	Ⓒ	Ⓓ

Accomplishments *2.1.3.d. Add and subtract efficiently and accurately with single-digit numbers. ***2.1.3.e.** Use a variety of strategies and representations to … subtract two-digit whole numbers. ***2.1.3.g.** Use estimation to justify the reasonableness of a computation.

Lesson 6-11   Name _____

1 There are 30 peanuts in each small bag of peanuts.
How many peanuts are in 3 bags?

33   60   63   90
Ⓐ   Ⓑ   Ⓒ   Ⓓ

2 Anne saw 43 monkeys at the zoo. Tony saw
17 monkeys. How many more monkeys did Anne see?

26   34   43   50
Ⓐ   Ⓑ   Ⓒ   Ⓓ

3 Joey bought these two stamps.
About how much did he spend?

90¢   80¢   60¢   30¢
Ⓐ   Ⓑ   Ⓒ   Ⓓ

The chart shows how many animals the children in Ms. Reid's class saw on a field trip. Use this chart for 4 and 5.

Animals	Deer	Ducks	Hawks	Foxes
Number	14	18	21	9

4 How many more ducks than foxes did the children see?

27   11   10   9
Ⓐ   Ⓑ   Ⓒ   Ⓓ

5 How many more hawks than deer did the children see?

35   17   13   7
Ⓐ   Ⓑ   Ⓒ   Ⓓ

Lesson 7-1   Name _____

1 How many vertices does a cube have?

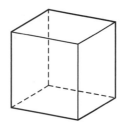

4	6	8	12
Ⓐ	Ⓑ	Ⓒ	Ⓓ

2 How many flat surfaces does a cylinder have?

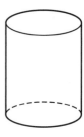

3	2	1	0
Ⓐ	Ⓑ	Ⓒ	Ⓓ

3 Which figure has 8 edges?

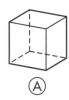

Ⓐ   Ⓑ   Ⓒ   Ⓓ

4 Which of the following is shaped most like a cone?

 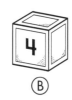

Ⓐ   Ⓑ   Ⓒ   Ⓓ

5 Fill in the blanks below to describe the tent Jamie used to camp in the Great Smoky Mountains National Park.

A pyramid has 5 flat surfaces, _____ vertices, and _____ edges.

Lesson 7-2　　Name _____

1 Which flat surface does a cone have?

Ⓐ circle

Ⓑ square

Ⓒ triangle

Ⓓ rectangle

2 How many square faces does a cube have?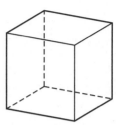

| 2 | 4 | 6 | 8 |
| Ⓐ | Ⓑ | Ⓒ | Ⓓ |

---

3 Which is a model of a rectangular solid?

Ⓐ　　　　Ⓑ　　　　Ⓒ　　　　Ⓓ

---

4 From which can you trace a circle?

　　　　　　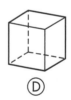

Ⓐ　　　　Ⓑ　　　　Ⓒ　　　　Ⓓ

---

5 From which can you trace a square?

Ⓐ　　　　Ⓑ　　　　Ⓒ　　　　Ⓓ

79

Lesson 7-3   Name _____

1 How many triangular faces does the following have?

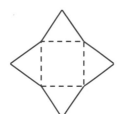

Ⓐ 1

Ⓑ 2

Ⓒ 3

Ⓓ 4

2 What solid figure would you make if you folded the following net?

Ⓐ cone

Ⓑ square pyramid

Ⓒ sphere

Ⓓ cube

3 How many square faces does the following have?

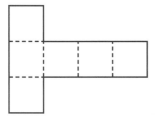

Ⓐ 2

Ⓑ 4

Ⓒ 6

Ⓓ 8

4 What solid figure would you make if you folded the following net?

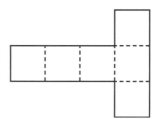

Ⓐ cone

Ⓑ square pyramid

Ⓒ sphere

Ⓓ cube

5 Which folded net makes a cone?

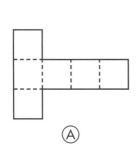 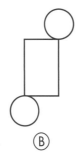 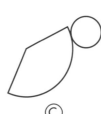 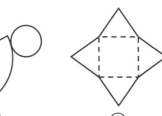

Ⓐ   Ⓑ   Ⓒ   Ⓓ

Lesson 7-4   Name _____

1 What is the shape made by joining two triangles, as shown?

Ⓐ parallelogram
Ⓑ trapezoid
Ⓒ square
Ⓓ hexagon

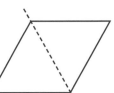

2 What is the name of this shape made up of two trapezoids?

Ⓐ parallelogram
Ⓑ trapezoid
Ⓒ square
Ⓓ hexagon

3 Kelly wants to put these shapes together to make a new shape. What shape can she make?

 Ⓐ    Ⓑ   Ⓒ   Ⓓ

4 John sketched the Governor's mansion in Nashville. Which two shapes make up his sketch?

Ⓐ   Ⓑ   Ⓒ   Ⓓ

5 Which new shape could be formed if these shapes were joined?

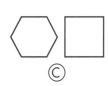

Ⓐ   Ⓑ   Ⓒ   Ⓓ

Lesson 7-5   Name _____

1 Why are the following shapes <u>congruent</u>?

Ⓐ They are the same shape and size.

Ⓑ They are the same shape and different sizes.

Ⓒ They are the same color.

Ⓓ They are different shapes and different sizes.

2 Which shape is <u>congruent</u> to this triangle?

Ⓐ

Ⓑ

Ⓒ

Ⓓ

3 Jane sorted blocks into pairs. Which pair is <u>congruent</u>?

        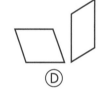

Ⓐ   Ⓑ   Ⓒ   Ⓓ

4 Which is <u>not</u> <u>congruent</u> to   ?

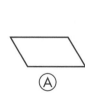      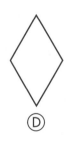

Ⓐ   Ⓑ   Ⓒ   Ⓓ

5 Are the two shapes in the pair <u>congruent</u>? Explain your reasoning.

_____

_____

Lesson 7-6   Name _____

1 Which describes how the shape is changed?

(A) slide

(B) flip

(C) turn

(D) no movement

2 Which describes how the shape is changed?

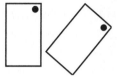

(A) slide

(B) flip

(C) turn

(D) no movement

3 Which pair of triangles shows a slide?

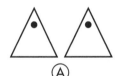 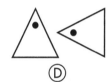 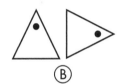

(A)   (B)   (C)   (D)

4 Which pair of figures shows a flip?

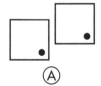 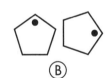  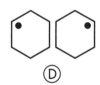

(A)   (B)   (C)   (D)

5 Ariel found this pattern in a painting at the Knoxville Museum of Art. Which shows the shape in its next position?

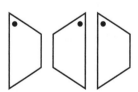

(A)   (B)   (C)   (D)

Lesson 7-7   Name _____

1 How many lines of symmetry does this shape have?

Ⓐ 0
Ⓑ 1
Ⓒ 2
Ⓓ 4

2 How many lines of symmetry does a square have?

Ⓐ 0
Ⓑ 1
Ⓒ 2
Ⓓ 4

3 Lin went apple-picking in Cross Plains. Which of her apples has two lines of symmetry?

  Ⓐ   Ⓑ   Ⓒ   Ⓓ

4 Which of the following shapes does <u>not</u> have a line of symmetry?

 Ⓐ   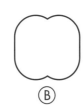 Ⓑ    Ⓒ    Ⓓ

5 Which of the following has the <u>most</u> lines of symmetry?

 Ⓐ    Ⓑ   Ⓒ    Ⓓ

Lesson 7-8   Name _____

1 Which shape has 4 angles and 2 lines of symmetry?

Ⓐ   Ⓑ   Ⓒ   Ⓓ

2 Which shape has 6 lines of symmetry and more than 3 angles?

Ⓐ   Ⓑ   Ⓒ   Ⓓ

3 Which shape has 8 edges and less than 6 flat surfaces?

Ⓐ   Ⓑ   Ⓒ   Ⓓ

4 Alyssa drew four sailboats she saw on Douglas Lake.
Which sail has 3 edges and more than 1 line of symmetry?

Ⓐ   Ⓑ   Ⓒ   Ⓓ

5 Write two sentences to describe
one of these shapes. Then circle
the shape your sentences describe.

_____

_____

85

Lesson 7-9   Name _____

1 Which describes the picture?

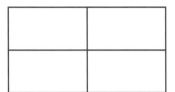

   Ⓐ equal halves

   Ⓑ equal fourths

   Ⓒ 2 unequal parts

   Ⓓ 4 unequal parts

2 Which describes the picture?

   Ⓐ equal thirds

   Ⓑ equal halves

   Ⓒ 3 unequal parts

   Ⓓ 2 unequal parts

---

3 Which picture shows equal parts?

  Ⓐ   Ⓑ   Ⓒ   Ⓓ

---

4 A bakery in Knoxville sells apple pies. Which pie below is divided into equal fourths?

  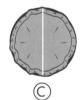 

  Ⓐ   Ⓑ   Ⓒ   Ⓓ

---

5 Which triangle is divided into equal halves?

  Ⓐ   Ⓑ   Ⓒ   Ⓓ

Lesson 7-10   Name _____

1 What fraction of the triangle is <u>shaded</u>?

Ⓐ $\frac{1}{8}$

Ⓑ $\frac{1}{4}$

Ⓒ $\frac{1}{3}$

Ⓓ $\frac{1}{2}$

2 What fraction of the square is <u>shaded</u>?

Ⓐ $\frac{1}{8}$

Ⓑ $\frac{1}{4}$

Ⓒ $\frac{1}{3}$

Ⓓ $\frac{1}{2}$

---

3 Which shape below shows $\frac{1}{2}$ <u>shaded</u>?

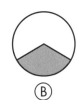

    Ⓐ   Ⓑ   Ⓒ   Ⓓ

---

4 At a pizza palace in Nashville, Martha ate $\frac{1}{3}$ of a pizza. Which pizza below has $\frac{1}{3}$ <u>shaded</u>?

 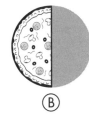 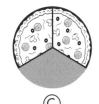 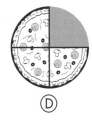

    Ⓐ   Ⓑ   Ⓒ   Ⓓ

---

5 Divide the rectangle below into four equal parts. Shade 1 part in with your pencil. Then, on the line below, write which fraction your picture shows.

_____

Lesson 7-11   Name _____

1 What is the fraction for the <u>shaded</u> part of the shape?

Ⓐ $\frac{1}{6}$

Ⓑ $\frac{2}{6}$

Ⓒ $\frac{3}{6}$

Ⓓ $\frac{4}{6}$

2 What is the fraction for the <u>shaded</u> part of the shape?

Ⓐ $\frac{2}{8}$

Ⓑ $\frac{6}{8}$

Ⓒ $\frac{2}{10}$

Ⓓ $\frac{2}{4}$

3 Which of the shapes has $\frac{5}{6}$ <u>shaded</u>?

Ⓐ

Ⓑ

Ⓒ

Ⓓ

4 Which of the shapes has $\frac{2}{9}$ <u>shaded</u>?

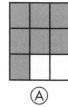
Ⓐ

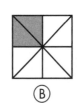
Ⓑ

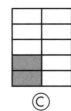
Ⓒ

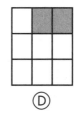
Ⓓ

5 For the Dogwood Art Festival in Knoxville, Barbara made a quilt with $\frac{4}{8}$ <u>shaded</u>. Which quilt could be hers?

Ⓐ

Ⓑ

Ⓒ

Ⓓ

Lesson 7-12   Name _____

1 About how much of Kristen's sandwich is left?

Ⓐ about $\frac{1}{4}$

Ⓑ about $\frac{1}{2}$

Ⓒ about $\frac{2}{3}$

Ⓓ about $\frac{3}{4}$

2 About how much of the juice is left?

Ⓐ about $\frac{1}{5}$

Ⓑ about $\frac{1}{3}$

Ⓒ about $\frac{1}{2}$

Ⓓ about $\frac{4}{5}$

3 Which describes the hexagon?

Ⓐ $\frac{1}{2}$ is shaded; $\frac{1}{2}$ is not shaded.

Ⓑ $\frac{2}{3}$ is shaded; $\frac{1}{3}$ is not shaded.

Ⓒ $\frac{1}{3}$ is shaded; $\frac{2}{3}$ is not shaded.

Ⓓ $\frac{3}{4}$ is shaded; $\frac{1}{4}$ is not shaded.

4 Which describes the square?

Ⓐ $\frac{1}{3}$ is shaded; $\frac{2}{3}$ is not shaded.

Ⓑ $\frac{3}{4}$ is shaded; $\frac{2}{3}$ is not shaded.

Ⓒ $\frac{3}{8}$ is shaded; $\frac{5}{8}$ is not shaded.

Ⓓ $\frac{5}{8}$ is shaded; $\frac{3}{8}$ is not shaded.

5 Jason is drawing the Tennessee state seal for a poster project. He has finished about $\frac{1}{3}$ of the seal. Which drawing could be Jason's?

Ⓐ

Ⓑ

Ⓒ

Ⓓ

89

Lesson 7-13   Name _____

1 What fraction of the shells is <u>shaded</u>?

$\dfrac{1}{3}$ $\dfrac{1}{2}$ $\dfrac{2}{3}$ $\dfrac{3}{4}$

Ⓐ   Ⓑ   Ⓒ   Ⓓ

2 What fraction of the group of stars is white?

$\dfrac{3}{4}$ $\dfrac{1}{2}$ $\dfrac{1}{3}$ $\dfrac{1}{4}$

Ⓐ   Ⓑ   Ⓒ   Ⓓ

3 What fraction of the group of letters are A's?

A A A A A
B B B

$\dfrac{3}{5}$ $\dfrac{5}{8}$ $\dfrac{5}{3}$ $\dfrac{8}{5}$

Ⓐ   Ⓑ   Ⓒ   Ⓓ

4 What fraction of the group of fruit are apples?

$\dfrac{3}{10}$ $\dfrac{3}{7}$ $\dfrac{3}{4}$ $\dfrac{7}{10}$

Ⓐ   Ⓑ   Ⓒ   Ⓓ

5 Regina baked some cookies. $\dfrac{3}{5}$ of her cookies were chocolate. $\dfrac{2}{5}$ of her cookies were vanilla. Which plate could be Regina's cookies?

Ⓐ

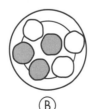
Ⓑ

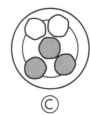
Ⓒ

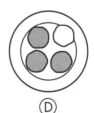
Ⓓ

90

Accomplishments *2.1.1.a. Count a set of objects to 100 using an efficient grouping strategy.
*2.3.1.a. Recognize [and] name ... three-dimensional geometric figures.
*2.3.1.c. Recognize shapes that have a line of symmetry.

Lesson 7-14   Name _____

1 How many lines of symmetry does this shape have?

0	1	2	4
Ⓐ	Ⓑ	Ⓒ	Ⓓ

2 Charles has 14 goldfish and 7 guppies. How many fish does he have in all?

7	21	28	31
Ⓐ	Ⓑ	Ⓒ	Ⓓ

---

3 Which of the shapes below has 0 edges, 0 vertices, and 0 flat surfaces?

| Ⓐ | Ⓑ | Ⓒ | Ⓓ |

---

4 The trunk of this tree is shaped <u>most</u> like _____.

 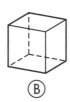   

| Ⓐ | Ⓑ | Ⓒ | Ⓓ |

---

5 At Cherokee Lake, Inez sketched 4 butterflies. Circle the butterfly that has 2 lines of symmetry. Then, on the lines below, describe how you knew which butterfly to circle.

_____

_____

Lesson 8-1   Name _____

1 What time is shown on the clock?

Ⓐ 9:40
Ⓑ 9:20
Ⓒ 4:45
Ⓓ 4:09

2 What time is shown on the clock?

Ⓐ 11:05
Ⓑ 11:25
Ⓒ 4:55
Ⓓ 5:11

---

3 Cyrus wakes up at 6:30. Which clock shows 6:30?

Ⓐ   Ⓑ   Ⓒ   Ⓓ

---

4 The second grade is leaving on a field trip to the Grand Ole Opry at 7:10. Which clock shows 7:10?

Ⓐ   Ⓑ   Ⓒ   Ⓓ

---

5 Louisa has to be home at 4:15.
On the clock draw the clock
hands to show 4:15.

Lesson 8-2   Name _____

1 What is another way to say 12:15?

- Ⓐ 15 minutes after 11
- Ⓑ quarter past 12
- Ⓒ 5 minutes after 12
- Ⓓ half past 12

2 What is another way to say 2:45?

- Ⓐ half past 2
- Ⓑ 45 minutes after 2
- Ⓒ 15 minutes after 3
- Ⓓ 45 minutes after 3

3 The clock shows what time school starts. What time does school start?

- Ⓐ 45 minutes after 6
- Ⓑ 15 minutes past 7
- Ⓒ half past 8
- Ⓓ half past 9

4 What time does the clock show?

- Ⓐ 35 minutes past 3
- Ⓑ 3 minutes after 7
- Ⓒ 15 minutes past 7
- Ⓓ 10 minutes after 7

5 Tobias is at a bluegrass concert. He is to meet his friend at 30 minutes after 11. Which clock shows this time?

Ⓐ

Ⓑ

Ⓒ

Ⓓ

Lesson 8-3   Name _____

1 A movie theater in Smyrna shows movies at 6:40. What is another way to say 6:40?

Ⓐ 20 minutes after 6

Ⓑ 20 minutes before 6

Ⓒ quarter to 7

Ⓓ 20 minutes before 7

2 John gets home from school at the time shown. What time does John get home?

Ⓐ 50 minutes after 3

Ⓑ 10 minutes before 3

Ⓒ 10 minutes after 2

Ⓓ 50 minutes before 2

3 What time does the clock show?

Ⓐ 30 minutes before 4

Ⓑ 40 minutes before 3

Ⓒ 20 minutes after 3

Ⓓ 30 minutes after 4

4 What is not a way to say 30 minutes past 10?

Ⓐ 30 minutes before 10

Ⓑ 30 minutes before 11

Ⓒ 30 minutes after 10

Ⓓ half past 10

5 Michele has a dance class at the time shown on the clock. On the lines below, write 2 ways to say the time shown.

_____

_____

Lesson 8-4   Name _____

About how long does each activity in 1–4 take?

1 Play a game of soccer

Ⓐ about 1 minute

Ⓑ about 5 minutes

Ⓒ about 1 hour

Ⓓ about 5 days

2 Camp in the Cumberland Gap

Ⓐ about 4 minute

Ⓑ about 2 hou

Ⓒ about 3 hours

Ⓓ about days

3 Pick flowers

Ⓐ about 45 minutes

Ⓑ about 5 hours

Ⓒ about 15 hours

Ⓓ about 2 days

4 Eat breakfast

Ⓐ about 3 minutes

Ⓑ about 30 minutes

Ⓒ about 10 hours

Ⓓ about 3 days

5 Stacey spends 1 hour reading a book. Robert spends 60 minutes at a swimming lesson. Which is true?

Ⓐ Reading a book takes less time than swimming lessons.

Ⓑ Reading a book takes more time than swimming lessons.

Ⓒ Both activities take about the same time.

Ⓓ Reading 1 page of a book takes more time than swimming lessons.

6 Beth spends 10 minutes cleaning her room. TJ spends 2 hours gardening. Which is true?

Ⓐ Cleaning takes less time than gardening.

Ⓑ Cleaning takes more time than gardening.

Ⓒ Cleaning and gardening take about the same time.

Ⓓ Gardening takes less time than cleaning.

Accomplishment *2.4.2.f. Solve problems involving elapsed time in hour intervals.

Lesson 8-5 Name ____________________

1 The clock below shows what time math class starts. Math class lasts 60 minutes. What time does it end?

Ⓐ 1:40

Ⓑ 1:50

Ⓒ 2:00

Ⓓ 2:10

2 The clocks show what time a TV show starts and what time it ends. How long does the TV show last?

Start

Finish

Ⓐ 30 minutes

Ⓑ 1 hour

Ⓒ 1 hour and 30 minutes

Ⓓ 2 hours

3 Ryan started washing dishes at 7:30. He finished at 8:30. How long did he wash dishes?

Ⓐ 1 hour

Ⓑ 50 minutes

Ⓒ 45 minutes

Ⓓ 30 minutes

4 Jill began practicing the violin at 4:35. She practiced for 1 hour. What time did she finish?

Ⓐ 4:45

Ⓑ 5:05

Ⓒ 5:35

Ⓓ 5:45

5 Casey and her father leave at 8:00 to drive to Knoxville. The trip takes about 60 minutes. Which clock shows the time they arrive in Knoxville?

Ⓐ

Ⓑ

Ⓒ

Ⓓ

Lesson 8-6   Name _____

1 The clock shows the time American Museum of Science and Energy opens. What time does the museum open?

Ⓐ 9 A.M.

Ⓑ 12:09 P.M.

Ⓒ 12:45 P.M.

Ⓓ 9 P.M.

2 The clock shows the time Ms. Rowe watches the evening news. Which time does she watch the news?

Ⓐ 3:30 P.M.

Ⓑ 6:15 P.M.

Ⓒ 6:30 A.M.

Ⓓ 3:15 A.M.

3 Ayana is eating dinner. Which clock shows what time it is likely to be?

Ⓐ   Ⓑ   Ⓒ   Ⓓ

4 Tom is walking his dog. What time would this most likely occur?

3 A.M.   3 P.M.   1 A.M.   11 P.M.

Ⓐ   Ⓑ   Ⓒ   Ⓓ

5 The clock shows what time Lily wakes up in the morning. On the line below, write the time Lily wakes up. Circle A.M. or P.M.

_____   A.M.   P.M.

Lesson 8-7   Name _____

Use this calendar for 1–6.

June 2004						
S	M	T	W	T	F	S
		1	2	3	4	5
6	7	8	9	10	11	12
13	14	15	16	17	18	19
20	21	22	23	24	25	26
27	28	29	30			

1 In Nashville, the Country Music Fan Fair is from June 11 to June 13, 2004. What is the last day of the Fan Fair?

Ⓐ Friday

Ⓑ Saturday

Ⓒ Sunday

Ⓓ Monday

2 Pravash's birthday is 1 week. from today. Today is June 3. What date is Pravash's birthday?

Ⓐ June 3

Ⓑ June 9

Ⓒ June 10

Ⓓ June 11

3 What date is the last Sunday in June 2004?

Ⓐ June 26

Ⓑ June 27

Ⓒ June 28

Ⓓ June 29

4 What is the last day of June 2004?

Ⓐ Tuesday

Ⓑ Wednesday

Ⓒ Friday

Ⓓ Saturday

5 What day is June 8, 2004?

Ⓐ Tuesday

Ⓑ Sunday

Ⓒ Monday

Ⓓ Wednesday

6 How many Tuesdays are in June 2004?

Ⓐ 8

Ⓑ 5

Ⓒ 4

Ⓓ 1

Lesson 8-8   Name _____

1 Bart spent 50 minutes at Graceland. Which is true about the time Bart spent at Graceland?

Ⓐ It was more than 5 hours.

Ⓑ It was more than 1 hour.

Ⓒ It was exactly 1 hour.

Ⓓ It was less than 1 hour.

2 Keisha spent one and a half hours making a necklace. How many minutes did she spend on the necklace?

Ⓐ 90 minutes

Ⓑ 60 minutes

Ⓒ 45 minutes

Ⓓ 30 minutes

3 How many hours are in 1 day?

Ⓐ 6

Ⓑ 12

Ⓒ 24

Ⓓ 36

4 Mary lived in Union City for 11 months. About how long did she live in Union City?

Ⓐ 1 day

Ⓑ 1 week

Ⓒ 1 year

Ⓓ 2 years

5 Find the pattern. What time will the next clock show?

Ⓐ 12:45

Ⓑ 12:50

Ⓒ 1:00

Ⓓ 1:15

Lesson 8-9   Name _____

The second grade class visited the Memphis Zoo. They made a table of their favorite animals. Use the table to answer 1–4.

Favorite Animals

Animal	Number
Snakes	|||
Birds	||
Bears	~~||||~~
Monkeys	||||

1 Which animal was the favorite of 5 children?

Ⓐ snakes

Ⓑ birds

Ⓒ bears

Ⓓ monkeys

2 Which animal was the favorite of 2 children?

Ⓐ snakes

Ⓑ birds

Ⓒ bears

Ⓓ monkeys

3 How many children are in this second grade class?

4	8	12	14
Ⓐ	Ⓑ	Ⓒ	Ⓓ

4 How many more children like the monkeys than like the snakes?

1	2	3	4
Ⓐ	Ⓑ	Ⓒ	Ⓓ

5 The table below shows second graders' favorite fruits. 3 children like apples and 6 children like oranges. Use tally marks to complete the table.

Favorite Fruit

Fruit	Number
Grapes	||||
Apples	
Oranges	

Accomplishments 2.5.1.a. Pose questions and gather data to answer questions.
*2.5.1.b. Read, interpret, and create tables using tally marks.

Lesson 8-10   Name _____

Lisa took a survey of her friends' favorite after-school sports. She made this table. Use Lisa's table to answer 1–6.

Favorite After-School Sport

Sport	Number
Basketball	ЖҬ ЖҬ ЖҬ
Dance	ЖҬ ЖҬ ‖
Football	ЖҬ ‖‖
Soccer	ЖҬ ЖҬ ЖҬ ‖
Tennis	ЖҬ ‖

1 Which sport did the <u>most</u> number of children choose?

Ⓐ basketball

Ⓑ dance

Ⓒ football

Ⓓ soccer

2 Which sport did the <u>least</u> number of children choose?

Ⓐ tennis

Ⓑ soccer

Ⓒ football

Ⓓ dance

3 How many children chose dance?

2	10	12	15
Ⓐ	Ⓑ	Ⓒ	Ⓓ

4 How many children chose football?

13	8	7	3
Ⓐ	Ⓑ	Ⓒ	Ⓓ

5 How many more children chose soccer than dance?

7	5	2	0
Ⓐ	Ⓑ	Ⓒ	Ⓓ

6 How many children in all answered the survey?

59	50	19	9
Ⓐ	Ⓑ	Ⓒ	Ⓓ

Lesson 8-11   Name _____

Use the Venn diagram for 1–4.

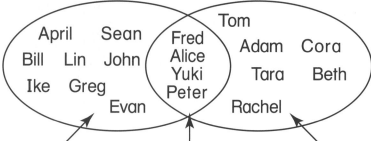

I like swimming.   I like both.   I like fishing.

1 How many children like both swimming and fishing?

4   6   8   12
Ⓐ   Ⓑ   Ⓒ   Ⓓ

2 How many children like only fishing?

2   5   6   8
Ⓐ   Ⓑ   Ⓒ   Ⓓ

3 How many children like only swimming?

4   5   7   8
Ⓐ   Ⓑ   Ⓒ   Ⓓ

4 How many children were surveyed?

20   18   14   12
Ⓐ   Ⓑ   Ⓒ   Ⓓ

5 Use the Venn diagram to answer the questions.

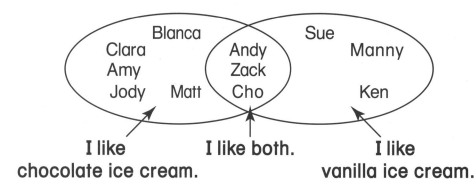

**I like
chocolate ice cream.   I like both.   I like
vanilla ice cream.**

_____ children like chocolate ice cream.

_____ children were surveyed.

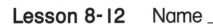

Lesson 8-12   Name _____

Sam and his friends went fishing in the Tennessee River. They
made a pictograph to show the number of fish they caught.
Use the pictograph for 1–5.

Fish Caught								
Bass	⊂◁	⊂◁	⊂◁					
Perch	⊂◁	⊂◁						
Pike	⊂◁	⊂◁	⊂◁	⊂◁	⊂◁	⊂◁	⊂◁	⊂◁
Trout	⊂◁	⊂◁	⊂◁	⊂◁	⊂◁			

KEY: Each ⊂◁ = 1 fish.

1 Which type of fish did they
catch the **most** of?

Ⓐ bass

Ⓑ perch

Ⓒ pike

Ⓓ trout

2 How many trout did they
catch?

Ⓐ 8

Ⓑ 5

Ⓒ 3

Ⓓ 2

3 How many more trout than
bass did they catch?

1	2	3	8
Ⓐ	Ⓑ	Ⓒ	Ⓓ

4 How many fish did they catch
all together?

18	17	15	13
Ⓐ	Ⓑ	Ⓒ	Ⓓ

5 What number sentence tells how many more pike they
caught than trout?

$8 + 5 = 13$	$5 - 3 = 2$	$8 - 2 = 6$	$8 - 5 = 3$
Ⓐ	Ⓑ	Ⓒ	Ⓓ

Accomplishments 2.5.1.a. Pose questions and gather data to answer questions.
*2.5.1.b. Read, interpret, and create tables using tally marks.
2.5.1.c. Create … bar graphs.

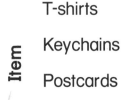

Lesson 8-13   Name _____

This bar graph shows the number and types of things sold one
day in the gift shop at the Casey Jones Home. Use the bar
graph to answer 1–5.

Items Sold at the Casey Jones Home

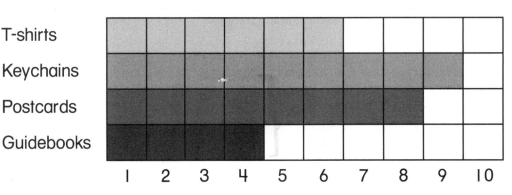

Number Sold

---

1 Which item sold the <u>most</u>?

- Ⓐ T-shirts
- Ⓑ key chains
- Ⓒ postcards
- Ⓓ guidebooks

2 Which item sold the <u>least</u>?

- Ⓐ T-shirts
- Ⓑ key chains
- Ⓒ postcards
- Ⓓ guidebooks

---

3 How many T-shirts were sold?

- Ⓐ 4
- Ⓑ 6
- Ⓒ 8
- Ⓓ 9

4 The shop sold 8 of which item?

- Ⓐ T-shirts
- Ⓑ key chains
- Ⓒ postcards
- Ⓓ guidebooks

---

5 Write a number sentence showing how many more
postcards than guidebooks were sold.

_____

Lesson 8-14   Name _____

A group of second graders went strawberry picking in Westmoreland. The line plot shows how many pints of strawberries they picked. Use the line plot to answer 1–6.

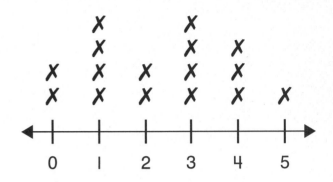

Pints of Strawberries Picked

Number of Pints

---

1 How many children picked 3 or more pints of strawberries?

  4   8   10   12
Ⓐ   Ⓑ   Ⓒ   Ⓓ

2 How many children picked 1 pint of strawberries?

  1   2   4   5
Ⓐ   Ⓑ   Ⓒ   Ⓓ

---

3 How many pints of strawberries did 3 children pick?

  0   3   4   5
Ⓐ   Ⓑ   Ⓒ   Ⓓ

4 How many pints of strawberries were picked by the <u>least</u> number of children?

  1   2   4   5
Ⓐ   Ⓑ   Ⓒ   Ⓓ

---

5 How many children went strawberry picking?

  16   14   9   5
Ⓐ   Ⓑ   Ⓒ   Ⓓ

6 How many children picked less than 2 pints?

  8   6   4   2
Ⓐ   Ⓑ   Ⓒ   Ⓓ

Lesson 8-15   Name _____

Use the coordinate graph to answer 1–5.

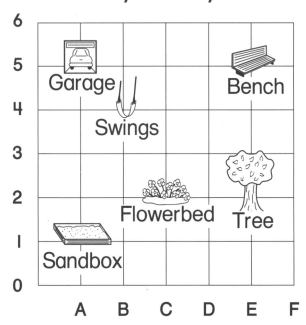

Tracy's Backyard

---

1 Which ordered pair tells the location of the flowerbed?

(C, C)   (C, 2)   (D, C)   (C, 1)
 Ⓐ   Ⓑ   Ⓒ   Ⓓ

2 Which ordered pair tells the location of the swings?

(B, 4)   (B, 0)   (B, 5)   (B, A)
 Ⓐ   Ⓑ   Ⓒ   Ⓓ

---

3 What is at (A, 1)?

Ⓐ sandbox

Ⓑ garage

Ⓒ flowerbed

Ⓓ bench

4 What is at (E, 5)?

Ⓐ tree

Ⓑ garage

Ⓒ swings

Ⓓ bench

---

5 Write the ordered pair that tells the location of the tree. Explain how you know.

_____

_____

Lesson 8-16   Name _____

Use the picture graph
to answer 1–2.

Books of Tickets Sold	
Brett	Ticket Ticket Ticket
Ann	Ticket Ticket
Jen	Ticket Ticket Ticket Ticket Ticket Ticket
Abbey	Ticket Ticket Ticket Ticket

KEY: Each Ticket = 5 Tickets.

1 How many raffle tickets did
Brett sell?

20   15   10   3
Ⓐ   Ⓑ   Ⓒ   Ⓓ

2 How many more tickets did Jen
sell than Ann?

20   10   8   4
Ⓐ   Ⓑ   Ⓒ   Ⓓ

Use the bar graph below to answer 3–4.

Sticker Collections

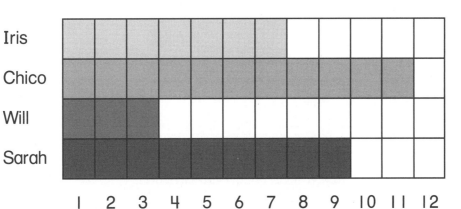

3 How many stickers does Iris
have?

3   7   9   11
Ⓐ   Ⓑ   Ⓒ   Ⓓ

4 How many stickers do Chico
and Will have all together?

6   8   10   14
Ⓐ   Ⓑ   Ⓒ   Ⓓ

Lesson 8-17   Name _____

1 Karam starts watching a movie at half past 8. The movie last 2 hours. What time does it end?

Ⓐ   8:30

Ⓑ   9:30

Ⓒ   10:15

Ⓓ   10:30

2 About how long does it take to get a haircut?

Ⓐ   30 minutes

Ⓑ   30 hours

Ⓒ   30 days

Ⓓ   30 weeks

3 What time does the clock show?

Ⓐ   20 minutes before 2

Ⓑ   20 minutes after 1

Ⓒ   10 minutes after 8

Ⓓ   50 minutes before 9

4 Jess started making popcorn at 6:15. The popcorn took 5 minutes to make. What time was the popcorn ready?

Ⓐ   6:10

Ⓑ   6:20

Ⓒ   6:30

Ⓓ   6:45

5 Lindsay and her mother leave at 5:00 to drive from Franklin to Columbia. The trip takes 40 minutes. Which clock shows the time they will arrive in Columbia?

Ⓐ   Ⓑ   Ⓒ   Ⓓ

Lesson 9-1   Name _____

1 About how many paperclips long is the hairclip?

Ⓐ about 1 paperclip

Ⓑ about 2 paperclips

Ⓒ about 3 paperclips

Ⓓ about 4 paperclips

2 About how many paperclips long is the sock?

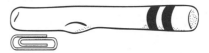

Ⓐ about 2 paperclips

Ⓑ about 4 paperclips

Ⓒ about 5 paperclips

Ⓓ about 6 paperclips

3 Which child is the tallest?

Ⓐ   Ⓑ   Ⓒ   Ⓓ

4 Which tree is the shortest?

Ⓐ   Ⓑ   Ⓒ   Ⓓ

5 Which earthworm is the longest?

Ⓐ

Ⓑ

Ⓒ

Ⓓ

Accomplishments 2.4.2.c. Explain the relationship between inches and feet.
2.4.2.d. Measure length to the nearest … foot … [and] inch.
***2.4.2.e.** Use strategies to make estimates of length….

Lesson 9-2   Name _____

1 What is the best estimate for the length of the desk?

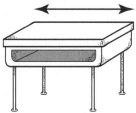

Ⓐ about 2 inches

Ⓑ about 2 feet

Ⓒ about 6 inches

Ⓓ about 12 feet

2 What is the best estimate for the height of a grandfather clock?

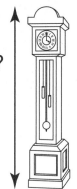

Ⓐ about 1 inch

Ⓑ about 5 inches

Ⓒ about 1 foot

Ⓓ about 5 feet

3 What is the best estimate for the length of the baby carrot?

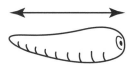

Ⓐ about 1 inch

Ⓑ about 5 inches

Ⓒ about 1 foot

Ⓓ about 10 feet

4 What is the best estimate for the height of a swing set?

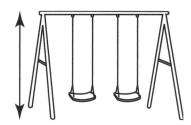

Ⓐ about 1 foot

Ⓑ about 1 inch

Ⓒ about 7 feet

Ⓓ about 7 inches

5 Marcel's arm is 24 inches long. Marcel's arm is how many feet long?

1	2	12	24
Ⓐ	Ⓑ	Ⓒ	Ⓓ

6 Judy's math book is 12 inches long. How many feet long is Judy's math book?

1	2	6	12
Ⓐ	Ⓑ	Ⓒ	Ⓓ

110

Accomplishments 2.4.2.c. Explain the relationship between inches and feet.
*2.4.2.d. Measure length to the nearest … foot … [and] inch.
*2.4.2.e. Use strategies to make estimates of length….

Lesson 9-3   Name _____

1 What is the best estimate for the length of this trail sign?

Ⓐ about 1 inch

Ⓑ about 3 inches

Ⓒ about 5 inches

Ⓓ about 7 inches

2 What is the best estimate for the height of the tulip poplar branch?

Ⓐ about 2 inches

Ⓑ about 4 inches

Ⓒ about 20 inches

Ⓓ about 40 inches

Use your ruler for 3–4. How many inches long is each?

3

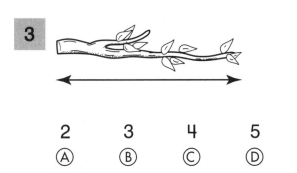

2	3	4	5
Ⓐ	Ⓑ	Ⓒ	Ⓓ

4

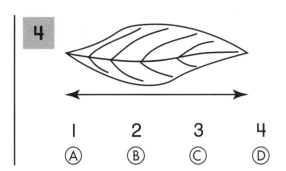

1	2	3	4
Ⓐ	Ⓑ	Ⓒ	Ⓓ

---

5 Which is longer, 1 inch or 1 foot? Explain.

_____

Lesson 9-4   Name _____

1 What is the best estimate for the length of the key?

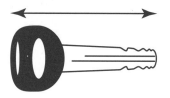

Ⓐ about 1 centimeter

Ⓑ about 2 centimeters

Ⓒ about 4 centimeters

Ⓓ about 6 centimeters

2 What is the best estimate for the width of this cube?

Ⓐ about 1 centimeter

Ⓑ about 2 centimeters

Ⓒ about 3 centimeters

Ⓓ about 4 centimeters

Use your ruler for 3–4.

3 How long is the model train car?

Ⓐ about 6 centimeters

Ⓑ about 8 centimeters

Ⓒ about 10 centimeters

Ⓓ about 12 centimeters

4 How long is the postage stamp?

Ⓐ about 7 centimeters

Ⓑ about 6 centimeters

Ⓒ about 5 centimeters

Ⓓ about 4 centimeters

Lesson 9-5   Name _____

1 Estimate the <u>perimeter</u> of the shape below.

Ⓐ about   2 centimeters

Ⓑ about   6 centimeters

Ⓒ about 12 centimeters

Ⓓ about 24 centimeters

2 Use your ruler to find the <u>perimeter</u> of the shape below.

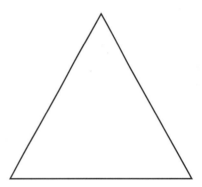

Ⓐ   5 centimeters

Ⓑ 10 centimeters

Ⓒ 15 centimeters

Ⓓ 20 centimeters

3 Estimate the <u>area</u> of the shape.

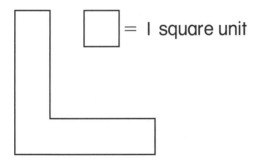

☐ = 1 square unit

Ⓐ   3 square units

Ⓑ   7 square units

Ⓒ 14 square units

Ⓓ 21 square units

4 Find the <u>area</u> of the shape.

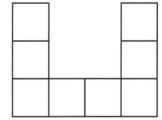

Ⓐ 4 square units

Ⓑ 6 square units

Ⓒ 7 square units

Ⓓ 8 square units

Lesson 9-6   Name _____

1 Which object holds the <u>least</u>?

Ⓐ

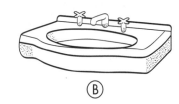
Ⓑ

Ⓒ

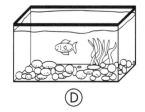
Ⓓ

2 Which object holds the <u>least</u>?

Ⓐ

Ⓑ

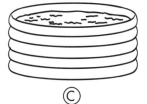
Ⓒ

Ⓓ

3 Which object holds the <u>most</u>?

Ⓐ

Ⓑ

Ⓒ

Ⓓ

4 For his science class, Dan is taking samples of water in the Tennessee River. Which container should he use?

Ⓐ

Ⓑ

Ⓒ

Ⓓ

Lesson 9-7   Name _____

1 How many cups hold the same amount as 4 pints?

2 cups = 1 pint

2   4   6   8
Ⓐ   Ⓑ   Ⓒ   Ⓓ

2 How many pints hold the same amount as 3 quarts?

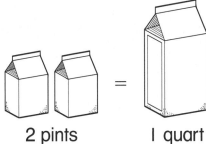

2 pints = 1 quart

9   8   6   3
Ⓐ   Ⓑ   Ⓒ   Ⓓ

3 How many pints hold the same amount as 10 cups?

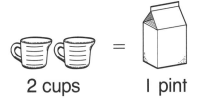

2 cups = 1 pint

5   7   10   20
Ⓐ   Ⓑ   Ⓒ   Ⓓ

4 How many cups hold the same amount as 4 quarts?

4 cups = 1 quart

8   12   14   16
Ⓐ   Ⓑ   Ⓒ   Ⓓ

5 An ice-cream parlor in Soddy-Daisy sells ice cream by the quart. Titus bought 2 quarts of strawberry ice cream. How many cups did he get? How many pints?

2 quarts: _____ cups

2 quarts: _____ pints

 =  =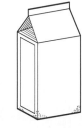

4 cups   2 pints   1 quart

115

Lesson 9-8   Name _____

1 About how many liters does this swimming pool hold?

- Ⓐ less than 1 liter
- Ⓑ about 1 liter
- Ⓒ about 8 liters
- Ⓓ about 80 liters

2 About how many liters does this fishbowl hold?

- Ⓐ less than 1 liter
- Ⓑ about 3 liters
- Ⓒ about 15 liters
- Ⓓ about 30 liters

---

3 Which object holds about 1 liter?

- Ⓐ
- Ⓑ
- Ⓒ
- Ⓓ

---

4 Which object holds more than 1 liter?

- Ⓐ
- Ⓑ
- Ⓒ
- Ⓓ

---

5 Which object holds less than 1 liter?

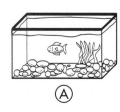  

- Ⓐ
- Ⓑ
- Ⓒ
- Ⓓ

Lesson 9-9   Name _____

1 How many cubes fit in the box?

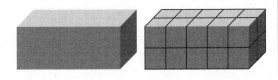

2	5	10	20
Ⓐ	Ⓑ	Ⓒ	Ⓓ

2 How many cubes fit in the box?

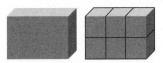

3	6	9	12
Ⓐ	Ⓑ	Ⓒ	Ⓓ

3 How many cubes fit in the box?

Ⓐ 6

Ⓑ 12

Ⓒ 18

Ⓓ 20

4 How many cubes fit in the box?

Ⓐ 4

Ⓑ 10

Ⓒ 12

Ⓓ 16

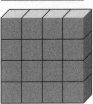

5 A gift shop at the Museum of Appalachia in Norris uses 2 different sized boxes to package souvenir T-shirts. If 20 T-shirts can fit into Box A, how many T-shirts do you think will fit into Box B?

Box A   Box B

_____ T-shirts

Explain how you know.

_____

_____

_____

Lesson 9-10   Name _____

1 Which picture shows an object that weighs the same as 10 cubes?

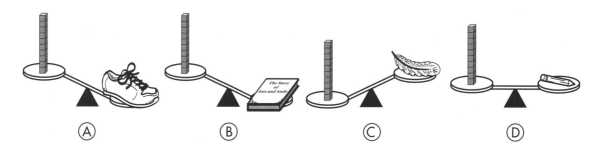

   Ⓐ   Ⓑ   Ⓒ   Ⓓ

2 Which object would make the scale balance?

   Ⓐ   Ⓑ   Ⓒ   Ⓓ

3 Which object weighs the <u>least</u>?

   Ⓐ   Ⓑ   Ⓒ   Ⓓ

4 Which object weighs the <u>most</u>?

   Ⓐ   Ⓑ   Ⓒ   Ⓓ

Lesson 9-11   Name _____

1 Which is the best estimate for how much the pear weighs?

   Ⓐ less than a pound

   Ⓑ about 1 pound

   Ⓒ about 6 pounds

   Ⓓ about 20 pounds

2 Which is the best estimate for how much the cat weighs?

   Ⓐ about 5 ounces

   Ⓑ about 7 pounds

   Ⓒ about 50 pounds

   Ⓓ about 70 pounds

---

3 Which object weighs more than 1 pound?

   Ⓐ   Ⓑ   Ⓒ   Ⓓ

---

4 Which object weighs less than 1 pound?

   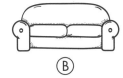   

   Ⓐ   Ⓑ   Ⓒ   Ⓓ

---

5 Which object weighs about 5 pounds?

   Ⓐ   Ⓑ   Ⓒ   Ⓓ

Lesson 9-12   Name _____

The second grade took a fieldtrip to the farmer's market in Milan.

1 What is the best estimate of how much a barrel of apples measures?

Ⓐ less than 1 kilogram

Ⓑ about 5 kilograms

Ⓒ about 25 kilograms

Ⓓ about 250 kilograms

2 What is the best estimate of how much a pumpkin measures?

Ⓐ less than 1 kilogram

Ⓑ about 5 kilograms

Ⓒ about 15 kilograms

Ⓓ about 150 kilograms

3 Which fruit at the farmer's market measures more than 1 kilogram?

         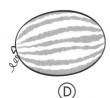

Ⓐ   Ⓑ   Ⓒ   Ⓓ

4 Which vegetable measures less than 1 kilogram?

Ⓐ   Ⓑ   Ⓒ   Ⓓ

Lesson 9-13   Name _____

1 What temperature does the thermometer show?

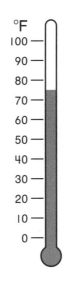

Ⓐ 50°F

Ⓑ 70°F

Ⓒ 75°F

Ⓓ 80°F

2 Walter is skiing in Ober Gatlinburg. Which is the best estimate of the temperature outside?

Ⓐ ⁻5°C

Ⓑ 15°C

Ⓒ 20°C

Ⓓ 25°C

---

3 At which temperature could you go swimming?

15°F   50°F   32°F   92°F
Ⓐ   Ⓑ   Ⓒ   Ⓓ

---

4 At which temperature could you go swimming?

2°C   5°C   10°C   25°C
Ⓐ   Ⓑ   Ⓒ   Ⓓ

---

5 It is 30°C today in Johnson City. Shade the thermometer to show 30°C. Then, on the lines below, write what clothes you might wear outdoors in this temperature.

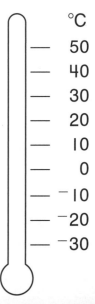

_____

_____

_____

_____

Lesson 9-14   Name _____

1 If you were to pick a shape from the bowl without looking, which shape are you <u>most likely</u> to pick?

Ⓐ triangle

Ⓑ square

Ⓒ circle

Ⓓ diamond

2 If you were to pick a fruit from the bowl without looking, which fruit are you <u>most likely</u> to pick?

Ⓐ apple

Ⓑ pineapple

Ⓒ strawberry

Ⓓ banana

3 Which color is the spinner <u>most likely</u> to land on?

red   gray   blue   white
Ⓐ   Ⓑ   Ⓒ   Ⓓ

4 Which color is the spinner <u>most likely</u> to land on?

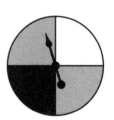

gray   orange   white   black
Ⓐ   Ⓑ   Ⓒ   Ⓓ

5 Which spinner is <u>most likely</u> to land on black?

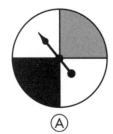   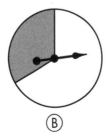      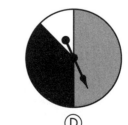

Ⓐ   Ⓑ   Ⓒ   Ⓓ

Lesson 9-15   Name _____

Adam counted the marbles in a jar.
Use his tally chart to answer 1−3.

Marbles	
Orange	卌 ‖
Blue	卌 卌 卌 ‖‖
Green	‖
Red	卌 ‖‖

1 What color are the <u>most</u> marbles in the jar?

orange blue green red
Ⓐ   Ⓑ   Ⓒ   Ⓓ

2 What color are the fewest marbles in the jar?

orange blue green red
Ⓐ   Ⓑ   Ⓒ   Ⓓ

3 Juan chooses a marble without looking. Which statement is true?

Ⓐ He is most likely to choose a green marble.

Ⓑ He is certain to choose a red marble.

Ⓒ It is improbable that he will choose an orange marble.

Ⓓ It is impossible that he will choose a purple marble.

4 Beth has a jar with 7 yellow marbles, 5 black marbles, 3 pink marbles, and 13 white marbles. Which color marble is it impossible for her to choose?

white   blue   pink   yellow
Ⓐ   Ⓑ   Ⓒ   Ⓓ

5 From which jar is it certain that you will pick a triangle?

Ⓐ

Ⓑ

Ⓒ

Ⓓ

Lesson 9-16   Name _____

1 Melissa had 25¢. She bought a notebook for 12¢ and a pencil for 8¢. How much does she have left?

Ⓐ 5¢

Ⓑ 13¢

Ⓒ 21¢

Ⓓ 45¢

2 Josh had 12 baseball cards. He bought 3 more. Then he bought 6 more. How many baseball cards does he have in all?

Ⓐ 15

Ⓑ 18

Ⓒ 21

Ⓓ 24

3 Kent brought 7 cupcakes to the school party and Cora brought 6 cupcakes. Later, Jim brought another 15 cupcakes. How many cupcakes were there in all?

Ⓐ 2

Ⓑ 6

Ⓒ 13

Ⓓ 28

4 Justine had 40 stickers. Then her uncle gave her 25 more. She gave away 15 stickers to her friends. How many stickers does she have in all?

Ⓐ 15

Ⓑ 50

Ⓒ 60

Ⓓ 65

5 Sabrina and Rob went to watch the Tennessee Walking Horse Celebration in Shelbyville. They saw 45 black horses and 33 grey horses. How many horses did they see? On the line below, write a number sentence for this.

_____

In the afternoon, 18 horses left the track. How many horses were left?

_____

Accomplishments *2.1.3.g. Use estimation to justify the reasonableness of a computation.
*2.4.2.d. Measure length to the nearest centimeter [or] foot....
*2.4.2.e. Use strategies to make estimates of length....

Lesson 9-17   Name _____

Rick and Susan packed a lunch and went fishing along the
Hiwassee River.

I Rick used the worm shown below. About how long is the worm?

I inch	3 inches	I5 inches	30 inches
Ⓐ	Ⓑ	Ⓒ	Ⓓ

2 Use your ruler. About how long is the
fishhook that Susan used?

2 inches	5 inches	8 inches	I2 inches
Ⓐ	Ⓑ	Ⓒ	Ⓓ

3 Susan caught 2 fish. One was I I centimeters long and the
other was I8 centimeters long. About how long were the
two fish together?

Ⓐ 7 centimeters   Ⓒ 20 centimeters

Ⓑ 9 centimeters   Ⓓ 30 centimeters

4 Use your ruler to measure the length
of this picture of Rick's lunch box.

Ⓐ about 6 centimeters

Ⓑ about 8 centimeters

Ⓒ about I2 centimeters

Ⓓ about I5 centimeters

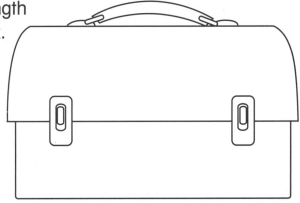

Lesson 10-1   Name _____

---

1 What is ?

4	40	400	4,000
Ⓐ	Ⓑ	Ⓒ	Ⓓ

---

2 How many?

2	22	200	2,000
Ⓐ	Ⓑ	Ⓒ	Ⓓ

---

3 What is one hundred more than

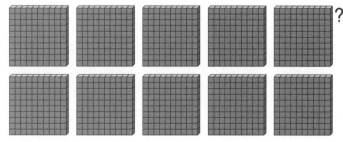?

8	600	700	800
Ⓐ	Ⓑ	Ⓒ	Ⓓ

---

4 What is one hundred less than

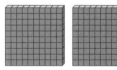?

9	10	900	1,000
Ⓐ	Ⓑ	Ⓒ	Ⓓ

---

5 Use models to show how many groups of one hundred are needed to make 1,000. Explain.

Accomplishments 2.1.1.c. Read and write numerals to 999.
***2.1.1.d.** Recognize the place value of a digit in numbers to 999.

Lesson 10-2   Name _____

1 How many hundreds are in this number?

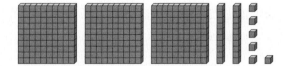

  2   3   4   5
 Ⓐ   Ⓑ   Ⓒ   Ⓓ

---

2 How many tens are in this number?

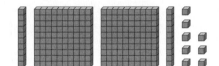

  2   3   4   8
 Ⓐ   Ⓑ   Ⓒ   Ⓓ

---

3 How many ones are in this number?

  1   2   3   4
 Ⓐ   Ⓑ   Ⓒ   Ⓓ

---

4 What number does this model show?

  12   354   453   543
 Ⓐ   Ⓑ   Ⓒ   Ⓓ

---

5 What is the number? The hundreds digit is a 7, the tens digit is a 2, and the ones digit is a 5.

  752   725   527   257
  Ⓐ   Ⓑ   Ⓒ   Ⓓ

Lesson 10-3   Name _____

1 Which is this number in standard form?

Ⓐ 632

Ⓑ 362

Ⓒ 236

Ⓓ 230

2 Which is this number in standard form?

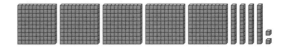

Ⓐ 245

Ⓑ 402

Ⓒ 500

Ⓓ 542

3 Which model makes a true statement?

Ⓐ 231 =

Ⓑ 413 =

Ⓒ 603 =

Ⓓ 123 =

4 Which is the correct expanded form of the number modeled?

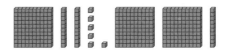

Ⓐ 300 + 30 + 6

Ⓑ 300 + 30 + 3

Ⓒ 1 + 2 + 6 + 2 + 1

Ⓓ 100 + 20 + 6

5 Find the missing number that makes this sentence true.

600 + ___?___ + 5 = 635

60   35   30   3
Ⓐ   Ⓑ   Ⓒ   Ⓓ

128

Lesson 10-4   Name _____

1 Use the model or mental math to solve.

$$2\underline{4}6 + \underline{3}0 =$$

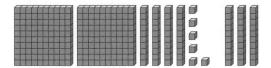

Ⓐ 236

Ⓑ 249

Ⓒ 276

Ⓓ 546

2 Use the model or mental math to solve.

$$\underline{1}23 + \underline{2}00 =$$

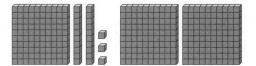

Ⓐ 125

Ⓑ 143

Ⓒ 223

Ⓓ 323

3 Use the model or mental math to solve.

$$2\underline{4}6 - \underline{3}0 =$$

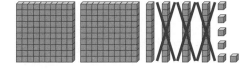

Ⓐ 206

Ⓑ 216

Ⓒ 276

Ⓓ 546

4 Use the model or mental math to solve.

$$\underline{8}23 - \underline{1}00 =$$

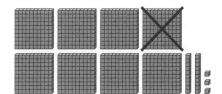

Ⓐ 923

Ⓑ 822

Ⓒ 813

Ⓓ 723

5 A farm in Virginia has 642 apple trees. A farm in Tennessee has 123 apple trees. How many apple trees are there in all? Explain, using models, how you found your answer.

Lesson 10-5 Name _____

1 Which statement is true?

Ⓐ 1,000 < 100

Ⓑ 367 > 246

Ⓒ 89 = 98

Ⓓ 747 > 874

2 Which statement is true?

Ⓐ 535 = 353

Ⓑ 535 < 353

Ⓒ 333 > 353

Ⓓ 353 < 535

3 Which statement shows that 742 is less than 842?

Ⓐ 842 < 742

Ⓑ 842 = 742

Ⓒ 842 > 742

Ⓓ 800 > 742

4 Which statement shows that 276 is greater than 270?

Ⓐ 276 < 270

Ⓑ 276 = 276

Ⓒ 276 > 276

Ⓓ 276 > 270

5 Jim used three blocks to make this number .

Karen used the same blocks to make a number less than Jim's number. Which picture shows Karen's number?

Ⓐ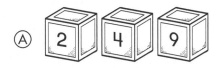

Ⓑ

Ⓒ

Ⓓ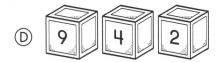

Lesson 10-6   Name _____

1 How many hundreds make a 1,000?

10   20   100   200
Ⓐ   Ⓑ   Ⓒ   Ⓓ

---

2 Choose the missing number.

500 + ___?___ = 1,000

50   150   500   550
Ⓐ   Ⓑ   Ⓒ   Ⓓ

---

3 What is the missing number?

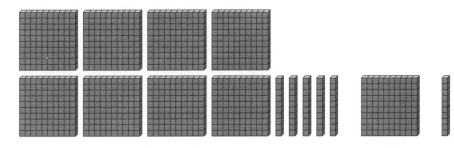

850   + ___?___ + 50   = 1,000

250   200   150   100
Ⓐ   Ⓑ   Ⓒ   Ⓓ

---

4 There are 600 pennies in the jar. How many more do you need to have 1,000 in the jar?

1,000   800   400   200
Ⓐ   Ⓑ   Ⓒ   Ⓓ

---

5 Tony has 300 points. To win the game he needs 1,000. On his second turn he received 250 points. How many more points does he need? Explain your answer.

Lesson 10-7   Name _____

Use the chart to answer questions 1–5.

Books Sold at Fair

Day	Monday	Tuesday	Wednesday	Thursday	Friday
Number	300	250	200	150	50

1 How many books were sold on Monday and Wednesday?

Ⓐ 500

Ⓑ 450

Ⓒ 300

Ⓓ 200

2 How many total books were sold on Tuesday and Friday?

Ⓐ 200

Ⓑ 300

Ⓒ 400

Ⓓ 500

3 On which two days were a total of 400 books sold?

Ⓐ Monday and Tuesday

Ⓑ Monday and Wednesday

Ⓒ Tuesday and Thursday

Ⓓ Wednesday and Friday

4 On which day were the least number of books sold?

Ⓐ Monday

Ⓑ Wednesday

Ⓒ Thursday

Ⓓ Friday

5 Which statement is true about the number of books sold?

Ⓐ Monday's sales were greater than Thursday's.

Ⓑ Monday's sales were less than Thursday's.

Ⓒ Monday's sales equal Thursday's sales.

Ⓓ Thursday's and Friday's sales combined were greater than Monday's.

Lesson 10-8   Name _____

1 Which number comes after 125?

100	110	120	130
Ⓐ	Ⓑ	Ⓒ	Ⓓ

2 Which number comes before 632?

631	632	633	634
Ⓐ	Ⓑ	Ⓒ	Ⓓ

3 What number is one after 724?

722	723	725	726
Ⓐ	Ⓑ	Ⓒ	Ⓓ

4 What number is one before 999?

1,000	999	998	888
Ⓐ	Ⓑ	Ⓒ	Ⓓ

5 What number is between 299 and 301?

290	300	310	390
Ⓐ	Ⓑ	Ⓒ	Ⓓ

6 Which number completes the pattern?

799, 798, 797, 796, ___?___

780	785	790	795
Ⓐ	Ⓑ	Ⓒ	Ⓓ

Lesson 10-9   Name _____

Use the chart showing distances between towns in Tennessee to answer questions 1–3.

Distance From Memphis

Town	Miles
Chattanooga	343
Clarksville	214
Johnson City	496
Knoxville	391
Nashville	212

1 Which town is closest to Memphis?

Ⓐ Clarksville

Ⓑ Knoxville

Ⓒ Nashville

Ⓓ Johnson City

2 Which town is farthest from Memphis?

Knoxville   Nashville   Chattanooga   Johnson City
   Ⓐ   Ⓑ   Ⓒ   Ⓓ

3 Order the towns from <u>greatest</u> to <u>least</u> distance from Memphis.

Ⓐ Nashville, Chattanooga, Johnson City, Knoxville, Clarksville

Ⓑ Johnson City, Knoxville, Chattanooga, Clarksville, Nashville

Ⓒ Knoxville, Chattanooga, Nashville, Clarksville, Johnson City

Ⓓ Johnson City, Clarksville, Knoxville, Chattanooga, Nashville

4 Which set of numbers is in order from <u>least</u> to <u>greatest</u>?

Ⓐ 321, 123, 103, 301, 201

Ⓑ 321, 301, 201, 123, 103

Ⓒ 103, 123, 201, 301, 321

Ⓓ 301, 201, 321, 103, 123

Lesson 10-10 Name _____

1 Which comes next?

△▲▲△△△▲▲▲▲▲△△△△△

Ⓐ △△△△△△

Ⓑ ▲▲▲▲▲

Ⓒ ▲▲▲▲▲▲

Ⓓ △△△△△△△

2 What is the next number in the pattern?

400, 500, 600, 700, _?_

Ⓐ 200

Ⓑ 300

Ⓒ 800

Ⓓ 900

3 Find the pattern. What are the missing numbers?

375, 365, 355, 345, _____,

_____, _____

Ⓐ 344, 343, 342

Ⓑ 335, 330, 325

Ⓒ 335, 325, 324

Ⓓ 335, 325, 315

4 Which is the next number in the pattern?

10, 11, 13, 16, 20, 25, _____

Ⓐ 27

Ⓑ 29

Ⓒ 31

Ⓓ 33

5 What statement describes the pattern?

100, 120, 140, 160, 180

Ⓐ The tens digit increases by 2.

Ⓑ The tens digit decreases by 2.

Ⓒ The hundreds digit increases by 2.

Ⓓ The hundreds digit decreases by 2.

Accomplishments *2.1.1.k. Compare two numbers using the appropriate symbols (i.e., <, >, =).
*2.1.1.l. Represent numbers to 999 in flexible ways using a variety of materials (e.g. 23 as 23 ones, 1 ten and 13 ones, 2 tens and 3 ones).

Lesson 10-11   Name _____

1 The Etowah Library has 450 books when it opened. The library bought 500 new books. How many hundreds of books do they have now?

3	5	7	9
Ⓐ	Ⓑ	Ⓒ	Ⓓ

2 Mike read 220 books in 2001; 240 books in 2002; 260 books in 2003; and 280 books in 2004. If Mike follows the same pattern, which number sentence would be correct for the number of books read in 2005?

2001 > 2005	2002 = 2004	2005 > 2004	2005 < 2003
Ⓐ	Ⓑ	Ⓒ	Ⓓ

3 Jackson Library bought 850 new books. Shelbyville Library bought 321 new books. Henning Library bought 724 new books. Pikesville Library bought 957 new books. Norris Library bought 98 new books. Which library bought the <u>greatest</u> number of new books?

Jackson	Norris	Pikesville	Henning
Ⓐ	Ⓑ	Ⓒ	Ⓓ

4 The Pigeon Forge Library bought 825 new books. How many hundreds of books did they buy?

2	5	8	825
Ⓐ	Ⓑ	Ⓒ	Ⓓ

5 Write and solve a story problem about a library. Use 4 numbers between 350 and 750. Write the 4 numbers in order from <u>greatest</u> and <u>least</u>.

Lesson 11-1   Name _____

Use mental math for questions 1–5.

1 **Solve:** $100 + 231 =$ _____

100	132	231	331
Ⓐ	Ⓑ	Ⓒ	Ⓓ

2 **Solve:** $241 + 438 =$ _____

641	678	679	700
Ⓐ	Ⓑ	Ⓒ	Ⓓ

3 **Solve:** $654 + 234 =$ _____

234	420	888	998
Ⓐ	Ⓑ	Ⓒ	Ⓓ

4 **Solve:** $500 + 478 =$ _____

1,000	978	178	78
Ⓐ	Ⓑ	Ⓒ	Ⓓ

5 **Solve:** $852 + 23 =$ _____

1,820	875	873	823
Ⓐ	Ⓑ	Ⓒ	Ⓓ

6 Find the missing number in the number sentence.

$300 + 500 = 600 +$ _____

100	200	300	400
Ⓐ	Ⓑ	Ⓒ	Ⓓ

Lesson 11-2   Name _____

1 Which number is closest to 672?

700   600   500   400
Ⓐ   Ⓑ   Ⓒ   Ⓓ

---

2 Which two numbers have a sum that is less than 500?

416 and 120   320 and 256   612 and 102   346 and 121
Ⓐ   Ⓑ   Ⓒ   Ⓓ

---

3 Which two numbers have a sum that is greater than 500?

489 and 279   234 and 103   400 and 78   332 and 159
Ⓐ   Ⓑ   Ⓒ   Ⓓ

---

4 Helen hiked 282 miles on the Cumberland Trail. James hiked 402 miles on the Appalachian Trail. About how many miles did they hike all together?

300   500   600   700
Ⓐ   Ⓑ   Ⓒ   Ⓓ

---

5 Which of these numbers completes the number sentence?

400 + 330 is less than 500 + _____

300   200   100   50
Ⓐ   Ⓑ   Ⓒ   Ⓓ

---

6 Which of these numbers completes the number sentence?

310 + 510 is greater than 640 + _____

710   510   310   110
Ⓐ   Ⓑ   Ⓒ   Ⓓ

Lesson 11-3   Name _____

For questions 1–4, find the sum, using models if needed.

1 Solve:

$$459 \quad + \quad 125 \quad =$$

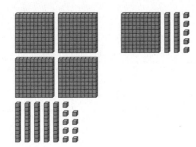

- Ⓐ 474
- Ⓑ 564
- Ⓒ 574
- Ⓓ 584

2 Solve:

$$361 \quad + \quad 273 \quad =$$

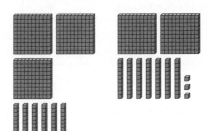

- Ⓐ 532
- Ⓑ 534
- Ⓒ 634
- Ⓓ 672

3 Solve: $443 + 492 =$

- Ⓐ 935
- Ⓑ 945
- Ⓒ 895
- Ⓓ 835

4 Solve: $193 + 524 =$

- Ⓐ 607
- Ⓑ 617
- Ⓒ 707
- Ⓓ 717

5 Mrs. Cash's class read 246 books first quarter. They read 228 books second quarter. How many books did they read in all? Solve and draw a picture of the base ten blocks used to solve the problem.

Lesson 11-4   Name _____

1 Solve:

Hundreds	Tens	Ones
□	□	
5	2	8
+ 4	3	4

952   962   974   984
Ⓐ   Ⓑ   Ⓒ   Ⓓ

2 Solve:

Hundreds	Tens	Ones
□	□	
6	5	9
+ 2	6	2

811   911   921   953
Ⓐ   Ⓑ   Ⓒ   Ⓓ

3 Solve:

Hundreds	Tens	Ones
□	□	
7	6	7
+	3	4

701   790   791   801
Ⓐ   Ⓑ   Ⓒ   Ⓓ

4 Solve:

Hundreds	Tens	Ones
□	□	
5	8	3
+	5	6

639   539   556   583
Ⓐ   Ⓑ   Ⓒ   Ⓓ

5 Solve:

```
   536
 +  29
```

555   565   575   585
Ⓐ   Ⓑ   Ⓒ   Ⓓ

6 Solve:

```
   851
 + 129
```

859   959   970   980
Ⓐ   Ⓑ   Ⓒ   Ⓓ

Lesson 11-5   Name _____

1 Solve: 246 + 662 = _____

Hundreds	Tens	Ones
☐		
+		

666   802   808   908
Ⓐ   Ⓑ   Ⓒ   Ⓓ

2 Solve: 491 + 191 = _____

Hundreds	Tens	Ones
☐	☐	
+		

491   591   582   682
Ⓐ   Ⓑ   Ⓒ   Ⓓ

3 Solve: 248 + 268 = _____

Hundreds	Tens	Ones
☐	☐	
+		

516   506   416   408
Ⓐ   Ⓑ   Ⓒ   Ⓓ

4 Solve: 182 + 182 = _____

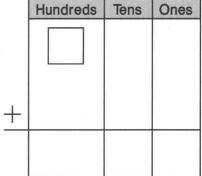

Hundreds	Tens	Ones
☐		
+		

182   282   264   364
Ⓐ   Ⓑ   Ⓒ   Ⓓ

5 Solve: 405 + 315 = _____

700   710   720   730
Ⓐ   Ⓑ   Ⓒ   Ⓓ

Lesson 11-6   Name _____

Some children took a survey. They picked their favorite place to visit. Use the graph to answer questions 1–4.

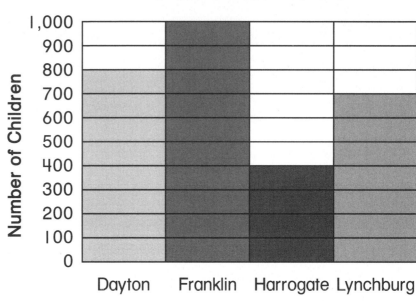

Favorite Place to Visit

Number of Children

1,000 900 800 700 600 500 400 300 200 100 0

Dayton   Franklin   Harrogate   Lynchburg

Place

---

1 Which city in Tennessee do <u>most</u> children like to visit?

ⓐ Dayton

ⓑ Franklin

ⓒ Harrogate

ⓓ Lynchburg

2 What city did 800 children choose as their favorite place ?

ⓐ Dayton

ⓑ Franklin

ⓒ Harrogate

ⓓ Lynchburg

---

3 400 children picked Harrogate. How many more children picked Lynchburg?

ⓐ 300

ⓑ 500

ⓒ 700

ⓓ 900

4 What is the title of this chart?

ⓐ Favorite Place to Visit

ⓑ Favorite Place to Play

ⓒ Number of Children

ⓓ Place

Lesson 11-7   Name _____

---

1 Count on or back to find the missing number.

$330 + \underline{\hspace{1cm}} = 400$

Ⓐ 100

Ⓑ 80

Ⓒ 70

Ⓓ 60

---

2 Count on or back to find the missing number.

$250 + \underline{\hspace{1cm}} = 650$

Ⓐ 200

Ⓑ 300

Ⓒ 400

Ⓓ 500

---

3 Count on or back to find the missing number.

$200 + \underline{\hspace{1cm}} = 580$

Ⓐ 200

Ⓑ 280

Ⓒ 300

Ⓓ 380

---

4 Count on or back to find the missing number.

$800 = \underline{\hspace{1cm}} + 500$

Ⓐ 100

Ⓑ 200

Ⓒ 300

Ⓓ 400

---

5 Count on or back to find the missing number.

$440 = 40 + \underline{\hspace{1cm}}$

Ⓐ 700

Ⓑ 600

Ⓒ 500

Ⓓ 400

---

6 Count on or back to find the missing number.

$510 + \underline{\hspace{1cm}} = 660$

Ⓐ 150

Ⓑ 200

Ⓒ 250

Ⓓ 300

Lesson 11-8   Name _____

1 Choose the best estimate for the problem.

$892 - 712$

- Ⓐ 100
- Ⓑ 200
- Ⓒ 300
- Ⓓ 400

2 Choose the best estimate for the problem.

$523 - 323$

- Ⓐ 200
- Ⓑ 300
- Ⓒ 400
- Ⓓ 500

3 Choose the problem that matches the estimate of 500.

- Ⓐ $775 - 676$
- Ⓑ $412 - 112$
- Ⓒ $875 - 375$
- Ⓓ $812 - 512$

4 Choose the problem that matches the estimate of 20).

- Ⓐ $189 - 110$
- Ⓑ $936 - 736$
- Ⓒ $631 - 295$
- Ⓓ $323 - 178$

5 Choose the pair of numbers that would give the correct sum of about 600.

- Ⓐ 512 and 189
- Ⓑ 612 and 23
- Ⓒ 724 and 124
- Ⓓ 230 and 315

6 Choose the pair of numbers that would give the correct difference of about 600.

- Ⓐ 512 and 189
- Ⓑ 612 and 230
- Ⓒ 724 and 124
- Ⓓ 330 and 235

Lesson 11-9   Name _____

---

1 **Solve:**   542 − 129 = _____

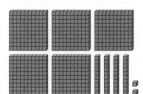

407   413   527   689
(A)   (B)   (C)   (D)

---

2 **Solve:**   648 − 263 = _____

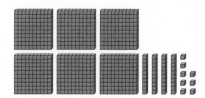

185   285   385   485
(A)   (B)   (C)   (D)

---

3 **Solve:**   944 − 735 = _____

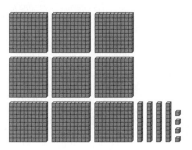

211   209   201   109
(A)   (B)   (C)   (D)

---

4 **Solve:**   375 − 119 = _____

356   306   256   206
(A)   (B)   (C)   (D)

---

5 The apple crate holds 456 apples. The children picked 470 apples. How many extra apples do they have if they fill one crate?

926   414   24   14
(A)   (B)   (C)   (D)

---

6 The children picked 470 apples. The parents picked 562 apples. How many more apples did the parents pick?

932   112   92   90
(A)   (B)   (C)   (D)

Lesson 11-10   Name _____

1 Solve:

Hundreds	Tens	Ones
☐	☐	☐
5	2	4
− 3	1	9

205	215	834	835
Ⓐ	Ⓑ	Ⓒ	Ⓓ

2 Solve:

Hundreds	Tens	Ones
☐	☐	☐
9	4	6
− 2	1	8

728	732	1,154	1,164
Ⓐ	Ⓑ	Ⓒ	Ⓓ

3 Solve:

Hundreds	Tens	Ones
☐	☐	☐
4	5	7
− 3	7	7

80	180	280	380
Ⓐ	Ⓑ	Ⓒ	Ⓓ

4 Solve:

Hundreds	Tens	Ones
☐	☐	☐
2	4	7
−	9	6

51	151	251	351
Ⓐ	Ⓑ	Ⓒ	Ⓓ

5 Will you regroup to solve the problem: $529 - 248 = ?$

Solve and explain.

Lesson 11-11   Name _____

1 **Solve:**   529 − 263 = ?

Hundreds	Tens	Ones
☐	☐	☐

   246   266   346   366
   Ⓐ   Ⓑ   Ⓒ   Ⓓ

2 **Solve:**   954 − 846 = ?

Hundreds	Tens	Ones
☐	☐	☐

   108   112   118   120
   Ⓐ   Ⓑ   Ⓒ   Ⓓ

3 **Solve:**   731 − 415 = ?

Hundreds	Tens	Ones
☐	☐	☐

   306   316   324   326
   Ⓐ   Ⓑ   Ⓒ   Ⓓ

4 **Solve:**   562 − 391 = ?

Hundreds	Tens	Ones
☐	☐	☐

   231   271   171   131
   Ⓐ   Ⓑ   Ⓒ   Ⓓ

5 **Solve:**   748 − 234 = ?

   500   514   600   614
   Ⓐ   Ⓑ   Ⓒ   Ⓓ

Lesson 11-12   Name _____

1 There are 365 people waiting for the Shockwave roller coaster. There are 523 people waiting for the Hypersonic XLC roller coaster. About how many people are waiting in line?

1,000 people   900 people   800 people   700 people
     Ⓐ   Ⓑ   Ⓒ   Ⓓ

2 Engine # 411 traveled 416 miles on Tuesday, and 528 miles on Wednesday. How many total miles did the steam engine travel on the two days?

1,355 miles   887 miles   944 miles   939 miles
     Ⓐ   Ⓑ   Ⓒ   Ⓓ

3 587 students go to Jonesboro Elementary School. 358 students have been to Fun City. How many students have <u>not</u> been to Fun City?

300 students   229 students   200 students   129 students
     Ⓐ   Ⓑ   Ⓒ   Ⓓ

4 Joey collects 348 tickets at Fun City. He wants to get a glow light that cost 950 tickets. About how many more tickets does he need?

500 tickets   550 tickets   600 tickets   650 tickets
     Ⓐ   Ⓑ   Ⓒ   Ⓓ

5 The Lenoir City Pool allows 500 people in the pool. If 97 people are in the pool, about how many more can still go in?

200 people   300 people   400 people   500 people
     Ⓐ   Ⓑ   Ⓒ   Ⓓ

Lesson 11-13   Name _____

1 Jaguars can weigh between 79 and 348 pounds. What is the difference between these two weights?

331 pounds	269 pounds	231 pounds	200 pounds
Ⓐ	Ⓑ	Ⓒ	Ⓓ

2 Asian elephants eat about 400 pounds of food a day. If Zoey the elephant has eaten 100 pounds during the morning, about how much more will she eat during the remainder of the day?

100 pounds	200 pounds	300 pounds	400 pounds
Ⓐ	Ⓑ	Ⓒ	Ⓓ

3 A small male African lion can weigh about 330 pounds. A large African lion weighs about 550 pounds. About how many more pounds does a large lion weigh, than a small lion?

100 pounds	200 pounds	300 pounds	400 pounds
Ⓐ	Ⓑ	Ⓒ	Ⓓ

4 A bald eagle was perched in a tree. The eagle caught a fish in the water 300 feet away. He then flew back to perch in the same tree. How far did the eagle fly?

300 feet	400 feet	500 feet	600 feet
Ⓐ	Ⓑ	Ⓒ	Ⓓ

5 A zebra ran 250 feet across the savanna. He then ran another 500 feet away from a safari truck. How far did he run all together?

950 feet	850 feet	750 feet	650 feet
Ⓐ	Ⓑ	Ⓒ	Ⓓ

Lesson 12-1   Name _____

1 Find how many apples there are in all.

- Ⓐ 2
- Ⓑ 3
- Ⓒ 6
- Ⓓ 8

2 Find how many slices of pizza there are in all.

- Ⓐ 5
- Ⓑ 10
- Ⓒ 15
- Ⓓ 20

3 Find how many there are in all.

10 groups, 10 in each group

- Ⓐ 10
- Ⓑ 20
- Ⓒ 50
- Ⓓ 100

4 Find how many there are in all.

20 groups, 5 in each group

- Ⓐ 100
- Ⓑ 200
- Ⓒ 300
- Ⓓ 400

5 Write a word problem about five groups with five items in each group. Solve the problem. Draw a picture to show your work.

Lesson 12-2   Name _____

1 Which is the correct multiplication number sentence for this addition number sentence?

$$2 + 2 + 2 + 2 + 2$$

□□ □□ □□ □□ □□
2 + 2 + 2 + 2 + 2

Ⓐ $2 + 2 + 2 + 2 + 2$

Ⓑ 2×4

Ⓒ 2×5

Ⓓ 2×6

2 Which is the correct multiplication number sentence for this addition number sentence?

$$3 + 3 + 3 + 3$$

OOO OOO OOO OOO
3 + 3 + 3 + 3

Ⓐ $3 + 3 + 3 + 3$

Ⓑ 3×2

Ⓒ 3×3

Ⓓ 3×4

3 Which sum is the same as the product of 3×6?

Ⓐ $6 + 6 + 6 = 18$

Ⓑ $3 + 3 + 3 = 9$

Ⓒ $6 + 3 = 9$

Ⓓ $3 + 3 = 6$

4 Which product is the same as the sum of $4 + 4 + 4 + 4 + 4$?

Ⓐ $5 + 5 + 5 + 5 + 5 = 25$

Ⓑ $4 \times 5 = 20$

Ⓒ $4 \times 4 = 16$

Ⓓ $4 + 5 = 9$

5 Mrs. Granger uses 7 apples to make one pie. How many apples would she need to make 3 pies?

$3 \times 7 = 21$ $2 \times 7 = 14$ $1 \times 7 = 7$ $3 + 7 = 10$
   Ⓐ   Ⓑ   Ⓒ   Ⓓ

Lesson 12-3   Name _____

1 Which multiplication sentence describes this array?

Ⓐ $2 \times 1 = 2$

Ⓑ $2 \times 2 = 4$

Ⓒ $2 \times 3 = 6$

Ⓓ $2 \times 4 = 8$

2 Which multiplication sentence describes this array?

Ⓐ $2 \times 1 = 2$

Ⓑ $2 \times 2 = 4$

Ⓒ $4 \times 2 = 8$

Ⓓ $4 \times 4 = 16$

3 What number completed this number sentence?

$2 \times \underline{\hphantom{000}} = 6$

3   5   9   18
Ⓐ   Ⓑ   Ⓒ   Ⓓ

4 What number completed this number sentence?

$\underline{\hphantom{000}} \times 4 = 16$

12   8   4   2
Ⓐ   Ⓑ   Ⓒ   Ⓓ

5 Which multiplication sentence describes this array?

Ⓐ $4 \times 1 = 4$

Ⓑ $4 \times 2 = 8$

Ⓒ $2 \times 4 = 8$

Ⓓ $4 \times 4 = 16$

6 Which multiplication sentence describes this array?

Ⓐ $3 \times 1 = 3$

Ⓑ $3 \times 3 = 9$

Ⓒ $5 \times 3 = 15$

Ⓓ $5 + 3 = 8$

152

Lesson 12-4   Name _____

1 **Solve:** $2 \times 6 =$ _____

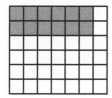

2	6	12	18
Ⓐ	Ⓑ	Ⓒ	Ⓓ

2 **Solve:** $3 \times 8 =$ _____

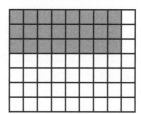

3	8	12	24
Ⓐ	Ⓑ	Ⓒ	Ⓓ

3 Complete the number sentence.

$2 \times$ _____ $= 18$

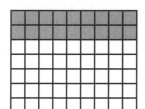

2	6	9	18
Ⓐ	Ⓑ	Ⓒ	Ⓓ

4 What number completed this number sentence?

$7 \times$ _____ $= 14$

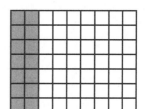

2	4	6	8
Ⓐ	Ⓑ	Ⓒ	Ⓓ

5 Which product is the same as $8 \times 2 = 16$?

Ⓐ $2 \times 7 = 14$

Ⓑ $2 \times 8 = 16$

Ⓒ $2 \times 9 = 18$

Ⓓ $2 \times 10 = 20$

6 Which product is the same as $6 \times 7 = 42$?

Ⓐ $7 \times 6 = 42$

Ⓑ $7 + 6 = 13$

Ⓒ $6 + 7 = 13$

Ⓓ $7 - 6 = 1$

Lesson 12-5   Name _____

1 Solve:

△△ △△ △△   6
 △   △   △   × 5
△△ △△ △△

△△ △△ △△
 △   △   △
△△ △△ △△

11	13	30	300
Ⓐ	Ⓑ	Ⓒ	Ⓓ

2 Solve:

          2
        × 7

14	16	18	20
Ⓐ	Ⓑ	Ⓒ	Ⓓ

3 Solve:

○○○○○○○   4
○○○○○○○   × 7
○○○○○○○
○○○○○○○

11	17	25	28
Ⓐ	Ⓑ	Ⓒ	Ⓓ

4 Solve:

          3
        × 9

29	27	15	12
Ⓐ	Ⓑ	Ⓒ	Ⓓ

5 There are 5 plates with 8 grapes on each plates. How many grapes in all?

Ⓐ $5 \times 8 = 40$

Ⓑ $5 + 8 = 13$

Ⓒ $7 \times 8 = 56$

Ⓓ $8 \times 2 = 16$

6 There are 6 children in line for tickets. Each child buys 7 tickets. How many tickets were bought in all?

Ⓐ $7 \times 6 = 42$

Ⓑ $7 + 6 = 13$

Ⓒ $6 + 7 = 13$

Ⓓ $7 - 6 = 1$

Lesson 12-6   Name _____

1 There are six students and each student has four markers. How many markers are there in all?

4   6   12   24
Ⓐ   Ⓑ   Ⓒ   Ⓓ

2 Four dogs are at the park. Each dog has two toys to play with. How many toys are there at the park?

4   6   8   10
Ⓐ   Ⓑ   Ⓒ   Ⓓ

3 Megan saw three clowns in the park. Each clown has ten balloons. How many balloons did she see?

30   15   10   3
Ⓐ   Ⓑ   Ⓒ   Ⓓ

4 The school store has seven different kinds of pencils. If Greg buys two of each kind, how many pencils will he buy?

2   7   14   20
Ⓐ   Ⓑ   Ⓒ   Ⓓ

5 The school playground has three areas for swings. Each area has five swings. There are seventeen students that want to swing. Are there enough swings for all the students? Explain.

_____

_____

Lesson 12-7   Name _____

1 There are eight bags and 24 whistles. Each bag will have the same number of whistles. How many whistles will be in each bag?

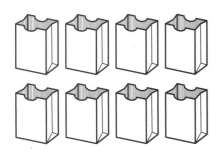

3	8	12	24
Ⓐ	Ⓑ	Ⓒ	Ⓓ

2 There are 24 pieces of candy. Four students want to share the candy equally. How many pieces of candy does each student receive?

24	12	6	4
Ⓐ	Ⓑ	Ⓒ	Ⓓ

3 There are 8 tickets. Each of two children has the same number. How many tickets does each child have?

2	4	6	8
Ⓐ	Ⓑ	Ⓒ	Ⓓ

4 There are 5 students playing a game. If the teacher has 50 game pieces, how many will each child receive?

45	27	15	10
Ⓐ	Ⓑ	Ⓒ	Ⓓ

5 Twelve children are looking at a bucket holding 144 pennies. If the bucket is dumped and each child has an equal share, how many pennies should each child receive?

24	14	12	2
Ⓐ	Ⓑ	Ⓒ	Ⓓ

Lesson 12-8 Name _____

1 Which division sentence shows 6 jellybeans divided among 3 bowls?

Ⓐ $3 \times 2 = 6$

Ⓑ $3 + 2 = 5$

Ⓒ $6 - 3 = 3$

Ⓓ $6 \div 3 = 2$

2 Which division sentence shows 15 pennies divided into 5 piggy banks?

Ⓐ $15 \div 5 = 3$

Ⓑ $15 - 5 = 10$

Ⓒ $15 + 5 = 20$

Ⓓ $3 + 5 = 8$

3 Which division sentence shows 16 flowers divided among 4 flower pots?

Ⓐ $12 \div 4 = 3$

Ⓑ $16 \div 4 = 4$

Ⓒ $20 \div 4 = 5$

Ⓓ $24 \div 4 = 6$

4 What number will make this number sentence true?

$18 \div 3 = $ _____

Ⓐ 5

Ⓑ 6

Ⓒ 12

Ⓓ 14

5 Elsie and her two friends had 12 sticks of sidewalk chalk to share. They each took 4 sticks of chalk. Will this solution work? Write a number sentence and explain by using a drawing.

_____

Lesson 12-9   Name _____

1 There are 12 books on the shelf. Four students want to take them home. How many books will each student take home?

Ⓐ 3

Ⓑ 5

Ⓒ 7

Ⓓ 9

2 William is playing with 20 blocks. He gives five to his sister. How many blocks does he have left?

Ⓐ 4

Ⓑ 5

Ⓒ 10

Ⓓ 15

3 There were 24 cherry tomatoes on the vine. Karen put eight in each basket. How many baskets did she have?

Ⓐ 24

Ⓑ 12

Ⓒ 8

Ⓓ 3

4 Stuart runs two miles every day of the week except Sunday. How many miles does he run in one week?

Ⓐ 7

Ⓑ 9

Ⓒ 12

Ⓓ 14

5 Three balls fit into each tennis ball tube. 21 balls are rolling around the tennis court. How many tubes are needed to put all the balls in a tube?

3   5   7   9
Ⓐ   Ⓑ   Ⓒ   Ⓓ

Lesson 12-10 Name _____

1 There are 12 passengers on the plane. Each passenger has two bags of luggage. How many pieces of luggage are on the plane?

12 pieces	24 pieces	36 pieces	48 pieces
Ⓐ	Ⓑ	Ⓒ	Ⓓ

2 The plane has 15 seats. 20 people want to get on the plane. How many people will be left waiting for another plane?

5 people	10 people	15 people	20 people
Ⓐ	Ⓑ	Ⓒ	Ⓓ

3 A 747 jet flew 324 people from Nashville to Dallas. Then it carried 256 people from Dallas to Nashville. How many passengers did the jet carry on those two flights?

Ⓐ 68 passengers

Ⓑ 268 passengers

Ⓒ 571 passengers

Ⓓ 580 passengers

4 The airplane has 9 passenger windows on each of the two sides of the plane. How many total passenger windows are there?

2 windows	9 windows	18 windows	27 windows
Ⓐ	Ⓑ	Ⓒ	Ⓓ

5 The Baker family has 4 pieces of luggage that each weigh about 40 pounds. About how many total pounds of luggage does the Baker family have?

40 pounds	80 pounds	120 pounds	160 pounds
Ⓐ	Ⓑ	Ⓒ	Ⓓ

TCAP Achievement Practice Test
Part 1

1 Solve:

$$44 \\ + 35$$

A 78

B 79

C 88

D 89

2 Solve: $6 + 7 = \underline{\hspace{1cm}}$

A 11

B 12

C 13

D 14

---

3 Solve: $18 - 9 = \underline{\hspace{1cm}}$

A 10

B 9

C 8

D 7

4 Solve:

$$57 \\ + 28$$

A 75

B 85

C 95

D 175

TCAP Achievement Practice Test

5 Solve: 47
           − 38

    Ⓐ   9

    Ⓑ 11

    Ⓒ 15

    Ⓓ 85

6 Solve: 35
           29
         + 11

    Ⓐ 64

    Ⓑ 65

    Ⓒ 66

    Ⓓ 75

---

7 Which picture shows the number in the box?

105

Ⓐ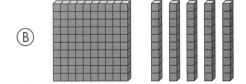

Ⓑ

Ⓒ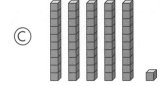

Ⓓ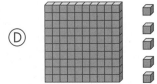

TCAP Achievement Practice Test

8 What is the fifteenth shape?

△ ○ □ ⬆ ⬇ ☆ ■ ♡ □ ▲ ⬡ ⬅ ➡ L T⌐ L ● ⬠ ♥

first

last

   Ⓐ △

   Ⓑ ⬅

   Ⓒ

   Ⓓ ●

---

9 Which solid figure can you trace to make the plane shape?

○

Ⓐ

Ⓑ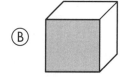

Ⓒ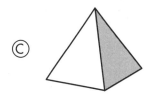

Ⓓ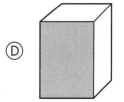

TCAP Achievement Practice Test

10 Pam started practicing piano at the time shown on the clock. She practiced for 2 hours. What time did she finish practicing?

ⓐ 1:00

ⓑ 3:30

ⓒ 4:00

ⓓ 5:00

---

11 Look at the bar graph.

Where We Like to Play

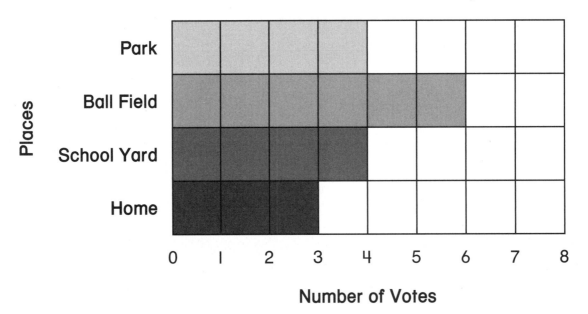

How many votes were for the park?

3 votes   4 votes   5 votes   6 votes

  ⓐ   ⓑ   ⓒ   ⓓ

12 There were 9 birds in a tree.
3 birds flew away.

Which number sentence tells how many birds are left in the tree?

Ⓐ $9 + 3 = 12$

Ⓑ $9 - 3 = 6$

Ⓒ $12 - 3 = 9$

Ⓓ $12 - 9 = 3$

---

13 Which number makes the number sentence true?

$328 < $ _____

Ⓐ 382

Ⓑ 318

Ⓒ 308

Ⓓ 300

TCAP Achievement Practice Test

14 Lois has these coins in her pocket.

How much money does she have in all?

Ⓐ 35¢

Ⓑ 45¢

Ⓒ 48¢

Ⓓ 53¢

---

15 Which fraction shows the part that is <u>shaded</u>?

Ⓐ $\frac{4}{1}$

Ⓑ $\frac{1}{2}$

Ⓒ $\frac{1}{3}$

Ⓓ $\frac{1}{4}$

TCAP Achievement Practice Test

16 What number comes next in this sequence?

300, 320, 340, 360, _____

Ⓐ 420

Ⓑ 400

Ⓒ 380

Ⓓ 340

---

17 Which number makes the number sentence true?

4 + _____ = 12

Ⓐ 5

Ⓑ 8

Ⓒ 9

Ⓓ 16

TCAP Achievement Practice Test

18 Which shape does <u>not</u> have a line of symmetry?

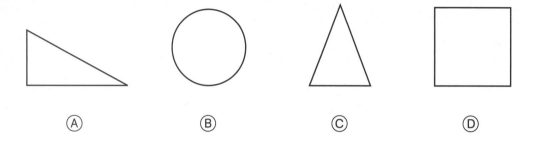

Ⓐ   Ⓑ   Ⓒ   Ⓓ

---

19 Which picture shows a turn?

Ⓐ

Ⓑ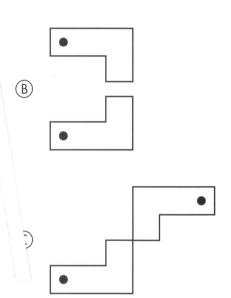

Ⓒ

Ⓓ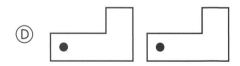

TCAP Achievement Practice Test

20 What is the length of the safety pin?

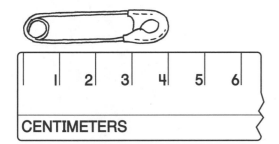

CENTIMETERS

Ⓐ about 1 centimeter

Ⓑ about 4 centimeters

Ⓒ about 5 centimeters

Ⓓ about 4 meters

---

21 What temperature does the thermometer show?

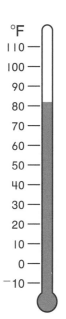

Ⓐ 78°F

Ⓑ 82°F

Ⓒ 90°F

Ⓓ 98°F

TCAP Achievement Practice Test

22 About how long does it take to play a soccer game?

Ⓐ about 6 minutes

Ⓑ about 60 minutes

Ⓒ about 60 hours

Ⓓ about 60 days

---

23 Tonya has a bag of marbles. The table shows how many marbles of each color she has.

Color of Marble	Number of Marbles
Red	卌 卌
Blue	卌
Yellow	‖
Green	卌	

If Tonya picks one marble from the bag without looking, which color is it <u>least likely</u> to be?

red	blue	yellow	green
Ⓐ	Ⓑ	Ⓒ	Ⓓ

TCAP Achievement Practice Test
Part 3

1 Solve: $5 + 7 + 5 =$ _____

     Ⓐ 12

     Ⓑ 13

     Ⓒ 17

     Ⓓ 18

2 Solve:

$$\begin{array}{r} 38 \\ -\ 20 \\ \hline \end{array}$$

     Ⓐ 58

     Ⓑ 28

     Ⓒ 18

     Ⓓ 8

3 Solve:

$$\begin{array}{r} 42¢ \\ +\ 48¢ \\ \hline \end{array}$$

     Ⓐ 70¢

     Ⓑ 80¢

     Ⓒ 90¢

     Ⓓ 100¢

4 Solve:

$$\begin{array}{r} 70¢ \\ -\ 34¢ \\ \hline \end{array}$$

     Ⓐ 34¢

     Ⓑ 36¢

     Ⓒ 44¢

     Ⓓ 46¢

TCAP Achievement Practice Test

5 Solve:

$$57 - 8$$

Ⓐ 39

Ⓑ 49

Ⓒ 51

Ⓓ 59

6 Solve: $19 + 4 = $ _____

Ⓐ 21

Ⓑ 23

Ⓒ 33

Ⓓ 113

---

7 Solve:

$$66 + 20$$

Ⓐ 68

Ⓑ 76

Ⓒ 78

Ⓓ 86

8 Solve:

$$97¢ - 88¢$$

Ⓐ 9¢

Ⓑ 11¢

Ⓒ 19¢

Ⓓ 21¢

TCAP Achievement Practice Test

9 Solve:

$$
\begin{array}{r}
7 \\
18 \\
+\ 34 \\
\hline
\end{array}
$$

Ⓐ 49

Ⓑ 59

Ⓒ 122

Ⓓ 129

10 Solve:

$$
\begin{array}{r}
44 \\
-\ 18 \\
\hline
\end{array}
$$

Ⓐ 24

Ⓑ 26

Ⓒ 34

Ⓓ 36

STOP

Key Vocabulary for TCAP Achievement Test Success

It is important to know the meanings of words and symbols on
math tests.

Key Vocabulary Checklist

☐ Use word parts to figure out the meaning of a word.

   Example: <u>Four</u>ths are fractions with <u>four</u> equal parts.

☐ Make up something to remember words or symbols.

   Example: The <u>larger</u> part of the symbol $<$ or $>$ always points to the
   <u>larger</u>, or greater, number.

SAMPLE

Which number
makes the number
sentence true?

$48 >$ _____

Ⓐ   46

Ⓑ   49

Ⓒ   84

Ⓓ   400

Think:
$>$ means "greater than."
Test each number to find a true sentence.
Is it true that 48 is greater than 46?

Compare the tens first. They are the same, so
compare the ones.

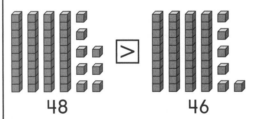

48   46

48 is greater than 46, so **A** is the correct answer.

---

1 Compare. Which symbol goes
     in the box?

     459 ☐ 288

     Ⓐ $>$

     Ⓑ $<$

     Ⓒ $=$

     Ⓓ $+$

2 Which number makes the
     number sentence true?

     $197 <$ _____

     Ⓐ 99

     Ⓑ 189

     Ⓒ 196

     Ⓓ 201